NEW ZEALAND

G·E·O·L·O·G·Y

Frontispiece   Haeckel Peak (2492 m) in the Southern Alps, exhibiting folded "greywacke" strata on its southern face. A large syncline is visible, with smaller folds in the core (centre).

Photo: D.L. Homer

NEW ZEALAND

G·E·O·L·O·G·Y

PATRICIA M. RIDDOLLS

formerly
New Zealand Geological Survey

Containing
GEOLOGICAL MAP OF NEW ZEALAND 1 : 2 000 000

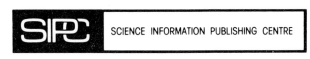

SCIENCE INFORMATION PUBLISHING CENTRE

DEPARTMENT OF SCIENTIFIC AND INDUSTRIAL RESEARCH

Wellington
1987

Edited for publication by Ian Mackenzie,
Science Information Publishing Centre, DSIR

Published jointly by
Science Information Publishing Centre, DSIR,
P.O. Box 9741, Wellington, New Zealand
and
New Zealand Geological Survey, DSIR,
P.O. Box 30-368, Lower Hutt, New Zealand

ISBN 0-477-02504-8

Cataloguing in publication:

RIDDOLLS, Patricia M.
    New Zealand geology : containing geological map of
New Zealand 1:2,000,000 / Patricia M. Riddolls. -
Wellington : DSIR Science Information Publishing
Centre, 1987.
    ISBN 0-477-02504-8.

I. Title.

UDC 55(931)

Contents

Abstract

New Zealand Geology

Patricia M. Riddolls

formerly
New Zealand Geological Survey

Geological map of New Zealand 1 : 2 000 000
Science Information Publishing Centre, Department of Scientific and Industrial Research,
Wellington, 1987

The 1 : 2 000 000 geological map of New Zealand is a synthesis of the more detailed geology presented on the 1 : 1 000 000 map published in 1972 and incorporates the results of recent geological mapping. The rocks of New Zealand are divided on this map into 47 units based primarily on time relationships, but Quaternary, igneous, and metamorphic rocks are subdivided on the basis of rock type and composition.

Economic mineral resources of New Zealand include metallic minerals, construction, manufacturing, and agricultural materials, mineral fuels, and groundwater. Hazards resulting from geological processes include landslide, earthquake, fault movement, volcanic eruption, tsunami, and flooding.

Keywords   Geological maps; 1 : 2 000 000; New Zealand; sedimentary rocks; metamorphic rocks; igneous rocks; geological history; deformation; mineral resources; land stability; geological hazards

Recommended bibliographic reference:

Riddolls, Patricia M. 1987: New Zealand geology.
    Geological map of New Zealand 1 : 2 000 000.
    Map (1 sheet) and notes. Wellington, New
    Zealand. Department of Scientific and Industrial
    Research.

Preface

The 1 : 2 000 000 geological map published in 1958 was a very popular map. At that time it was the most up to date synthesis of New Zealand geology and the only detailed map showing the whole country on one piece of paper. Its size made it an ideal wall map, and as such has been used extensively in classrooms and lecture theatres, and for display. The text to accompany the 1958 map (written by Grindley, Harrington, & Wood) was published in 1959 as *New Zealand Geological Survey bulletin 66*, and was reprinted in 1961. The 1 : 2 000 000 map was superseded in 1972 by the 1 : 1 000 000 map which showed greater detail, and was up to date. Continued requests for the 1 : 2 000 000 map, despite the availability of more modern maps, indicated a real need for a new map and a simple descriptive text.

This new edition draws on already published maps and information for its content, and attempts to show the geology of New Zealand as clearly as possible for the scale used. Because of the complex nature of the geology, many areas of rock are simply too small to show. Choices have been made and where a particular area of rock was considered to be important, it was enlarged on the map. Emphasis has been placed on the clearly visible aspects of geology. The large areas of blue and mauve readily identify the axial ranges, the areas of red and orange pick out the volcanic plateau area of the North Island, and the ubiquitous areas of yellow show the deposits of the Quaternary Period, a period which has had such an impact on our present-day topography. For reasons of clarity only those fault lines that have a clear impact on our topography and a history of recent movement have been included. Selected offshore drillholes are shown in order to demonstrate the continuity of past geological environments beyond the present-day coastline.

The text purports to describe the geology of New Zealand in a simple chronological fashion. It describes the rock types, the environments they were created in, and the deformation they subsequently suffered. It is written with the non-professional reader in mind with a general avoidance of technical terms, but as this is not entirely feasible a glossary is included. Basically the text describes the map, and just as every rock unit cannot be shown on the map every regional variation cannot be described. The last section deals with mineral resources and geological hazards (how geology affects our everyday lives); this is, necessarily, only a brief introduction to these topics. I have attempted to explain geological concepts as simply and concisely as possible. Many geological concepts, however, are very complex and involve a number of hypotheses. Thus some explanations will not satisfy all readers, as alternative interpretations of geological data are often possible. I have not detailed major geological theories such as plate tectonics, as these are adequately dealt with in recently published books; instead the text is mainly descriptive, with the explanation in the introduction intended to help the reader understand the descriptive part more fully. It should also be noted that the manuscript was written to tie in with authoritative books and texts available at the time (1981). There has been no attempt to systematically update the publication, although where feasible some recent information has been included.

I hope that this publication will prove to be a comprehensive introduction to New Zealand geology and that it will stimulate interest in finding out more from the suggested reading list included.

Patricia Riddolls

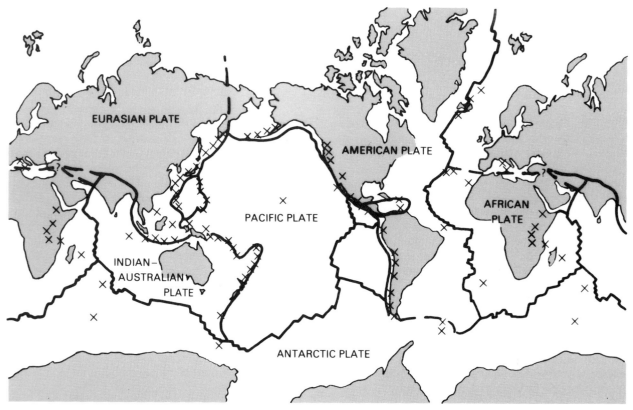

Figure 1 Disposition of crustal plates and their relation to volcanic activity. (Volcanic activity areas are marked with ×.)

Figure 2 Uplifted peneplain developed on schist in Central Otago. Note residual rocky outcrops (tors).   *Photo: D.L. Homer*

Introduction

The following account is a simple description of the geology of the New Zealand region as shown on the accompanying map. The region includes not only the main islands, Chatham, and Auckland islands, but also the surrounding continental shelf, an area of sea bottom which gently slopes to about 200 metres below sea level. The shelf is an integral part of the New Zealand region, a part which at present is below sea level, but in the past has been land. The land and continental shelf areas together have had a long and varied geological history; a history of see-sawing distribution of land and sea, of quiescent periods climaxed by powerful mountain building phases, of vast sediment-collecting ocean troughs and of small isolated basins. They have also undergone many climatic changes, varying from tropical heat to chilling ice ages. The distribution and nature of the rocks in New Zealand at the present-day reflect the events of the past. Thus the detailed study of the rocks enables us to build up a geological history; but there remain many gaps in our knowledge and the rocks still hold the secrets.

Geological setting

The New Zealand region lies in the far southwest of the Pacific Ocean astride a distinct belt of volcanic and earthquake activity (see Fig. 1) that surrounds the Pacific Ocean. This is the Pacific Mobile Belt or "Ring of Fire" and the activity results from the structure of the earth's crust. The crust is made up of a number of segments called plates (Fig. 1), which move relative to one another in response to forces deep within the earth. The plates may rub past one another, one may be forced down below another, or they may buckle at the edges as they meet head on. Wherever there is a plate boundary there is geological activity of a volcanic or tectonic nature. New Zealand straddles the boundary between the Pacific and Indian–Australian plates. To the north of New Zealand and beneath the eastern North Island, the thin, dense, Pacific plate moves down beneath the thicker, lighter Indian–Australian plate in a process known as subduction; within the South Island the plate margin is marked by the Alpine Fault and here the plates rub past each other horizontally; while south of New Zealand the Indian–Australian plate is forced below the Pacific plate. Plate movement results in volcanic activity in the North Island and in earthquakes that are felt throughout the country.

Topography and its relation to geology

Northwest Nelson and Fiordland are rugged mountainous areas formed of very hard rocks, which are the oldest in New Zealand. Their present mountainous form results not only from recent mountain building, but also from their greater resistance to erosion.

The Southern Alps and the axial ranges of the North Island form the "backbone" of New Zealand. These mountains comprise mainly hard sandstone and mudstone, collectively known as "greywacke", of Mesozoic age (see frontispiece), but the southern and western parts of the Southern Alps are formed of schist. The uplift of these ranges began 15 million years ago and has accelerated in the last few million years. The total amount of uplift in that period has been estimated to be in the order of 20 000 metres, but continuing erosion is responsible for the present height (up to 4000 m) as well as the dissected nature of the country.

A feature of the Central Otago area is the flat, even-topped, rather subdued, schist topography (Fig. 2), commonly with rocky outcrops (tors). About 70 million years ago this part of New Zealand was reduced by erosion to a nearly level plain (peneplain) close to sea level. This level surface has been particularly well preserved as it has been only gently uplifted and tilted rather than complexly deformed.

A great proportion of the southern part of the North Island is formed of rather soft Tertiary rocks. The rocks are very similar in character throughout the area: blue-grey sandstone or mudstone, popularly known as "papa". They form a very characteristic topography of steep slopes and sharp ridges (Fig. 3), reflecting the easily erodible nature of the rock. Harder rock types within them, such as limestone, stand out as prominent scarps, particularly in Hawkes Bay and the Wairarapa.

Limestone may have a dramatic effect on topography, commonly forming steep bare bluffs. It is soluble in water which enables erosion to take place along planar defects in the rock resulting in strange looking "karst" landforms (Fig. 4, see Fig. 18). Sinkholes (Fig. 5) occur where streams disappear below the surface to join extensive underground drainage systems, or where collapse of cave roofs has resulted from dissolution of the rock. Caves, of course, are common in limestone country. Some systems continue for many kilometres. The best examples of limestone formations are near Te Kuiti in the North Island, and in Northwest Nelson and Oamaru in the South Island.

The cone-like silhouettes of volcanoes in Taranaki and Tongariro National Park dominate the topography, while further north equally remarkable flat-topped plateau areas (Fig. 6) are formed by ignimbrite flows. Volcanic cones are also prominent in the Auckland region, Bay of Plenty (Fig. 7), and in some areas of Northland. Much of the topography in the northern half of the North Island has been modified by deposits of ash from repeated volcanic activity in the past million years. Many lakes in the central volcanic region are in the craters of previously active volcanic centres.

The climate of the last million years (a time of successive cooling and warming) has had a major effect on present-day topography. Glaciers carved out huge U-shaped valleys in the mountains, and fans of alluvial detritus eroded from the bare mountain slopes

Figure 3 Typical finely dissected topography of the Wanganui River area, eroded into gently dipping, soft, Tertiary sandstone and mudstone. *Photo: D.L. Homer*

Figure 4 Limestone of Oligocene age, showing fluting on rocky outcrops in the Waro Reserve, north of Whangarei. Bedding planes are visible as almost horizontal layers at lower centre. *Photo: S.N. Beatus*

8

Figure 5 Spectacular development of sinkholes in Oligocene limestone at Pareora near Timaru. The underground courses of several creeks may be seen from chains of sinkholes. *Photo: S.N. Beatus*

built up during the colder times. (The Canterbury Plains were built from glacial outwash, Fig. 8.) During warmer periods sea level rose and cut coastal terraces in rocks and alluvial debris (Fig. 9); successive rises and falls of the sea to different levels formed the flights of terraces seen in the river valleys and around the coast. When sea level was low, wide areas of sand exposed to the wind were blown into dunes. They form the extensive dune country of the west coast of the North Island (Fig. 10) and Northland.

The Marlborough Sounds, Fiordland, and parts of the north and west of the North Island are examples of drowned topography (Fig. 11). River and glacier valley systems established at times of low sea level were subsequently inundated by the sea when it rose to its present level.

Classes of rock

The rock units shown on the geological map are divided into three major classes based on their mode of formation:

The first class, **sedimentary rock**, results from deposition and consolidation of particles mostly eroded from an adjacent land area. Different sources of material and depositional environments result in different types of sedimentary rock, such as sandstone, mudstone, and limestone. Most New Zealand sedimentary rocks are mudstone and sandstone that were deposited beneath the sea. A sedimentary rock derived from ejected volcanic fragments (e.g., ash) is called tuff. Some sedimentary rocks, such as chert and certain limestones, are chemical precipitates.

The second class, **igneous rock**, forms when molten rock (magma) from deep within the earth's crust cools after being intruded into existing rocks or sediments, or after being extruded on to the surface. The rocks are classified as acid, intermediate, or basic, according to the amount of silica they contain. Acid (silica-rich) igneous rocks are light in colour, whereas the basic (silica-poor) igneous rocks are darker. There is a secondary two-fold division of igneous rocks into: **plutonic rocks** which are intruded at depth, cool slowly, and are coarse grained (granite is an example of an acid plutonic rock, diorite is intermediate, and gabbro

9

Figure 6 The Mamaku Plateau in the Bay of Plenty is a good example of the topography formed by an ignimbrite flow.   *Photo: D.L. Homer*

Figure 7 Mount Edgecumbe in the Bay of Plenty has the typical volcanic cone form. This andesitic volcano last erupted 900 years ago and is not considered extinct. The town of Kawerau is visible on the alluvial flat to the left of Mount Edgecumbe.   *Photo: D.L. Homer*

10

Figure 8 The Rakaia River flowing through the Canterbury Plains. Note the terraces at different levels and the clear braided pattern on a terrace to the left of the river, clearly indicating that this was once the river bed. *N.Z.G.S. photo*

Figure 9 Marine terraces southwest of Kaiwhata River mouth (foreground), coastal Wairarapa. The terrace at left margin (middle distance) is about 80 000 years old, and the highest terrace (left and right background) about 100 000 years old. These remnants of previous sea levels have been tectonically raised to their present level. *Photo: D.L. Homer*

is basic); and **volcanic rocks** which are extruded on to the land surface, or beneath the sea, and cool quickly to form fine grained and sometimes glassy rocks. Acid volcanic rocks include rhyolite, ignimbrite, and pumice, the last two being formed when the lava was particularly gaseous and explosive in nature. Common intermediate and basic lavas are andesite and basalt respectively.

The third class, **metamorphic rock** (schist and gneiss), have been recrystallised under conditions of high temperature, pressure, or both. They vary in type depending on the nature of the parent rock (either sedimentary or igneous) and the intensity and type of metamorphism. Characteristic minerals form under certain conditions of temperature and pressure. For example, chlorite tends to crystallise in rocks metamorphosed at low to moderate temperatures and pressures, and biotite and garnet at somewhat higher temperatures and pressures. Gneiss forms at deep levels in the crust under conditions of high temperature and pressure.

Geological processes

The processes of rock formation are never ending. Sedimentation is cyclical, particles being continually eroded, transported, deposited, and cemented to form new rock that may later be uplifted so that erosion starts the cycle again. The uplift and erosional episodes of the sedimentary cycle make it impossible for any one area to have a rock sequence representing the whole of geological time. Only when an area is totally submerged beneath the sea can there be continuous sedimentation providing a complete time record, and even then there may be gaps (unconformities) resulting from removal of sediments by strong bottom currents, or periods of non-deposition. When an area is above sea level, sporadic terrestrial deposits such as fluvial sediments and coal measures, and igneous rocks may be the only representatives of that time.

Compressional and tensional forces produce movement of the earth's crust (tectonism), causing it to buckle, warp, or crack. Long-continued downwarp-

12

Figure 10 Quaternary sand dunes, clearly showing a parabolic form indicating the direction of the wind (from lower left to top centre). Lake Horowhenua, formed by the advancing dunes, is in the background. *Photo: D.L. Homer*

Figure 11 Drowned glacial topography in Fiordland. The steep rugged mountains are composed of lower Paleozoic schist and gneiss. This view is the Hall Arm of Doubtful Sound. *N.Z.G.S. photo*

Millions of years	ERA	PERIOD		EPOCH	N.Z. EVENT
	CENOZOIC	QUATERNARY		HOLOCENE	KAIKOURA OROGENY
0				PLEISTOCENE	
		TERTIARY		PLIOCENE	
				MIOCENE	DEPOSITIONAL PHASE
				OLIGOCENE	
50				EOCENE	
				PALEOCENE	
	MESOZOIC	CRETACEOUS		LATE	
100					
				EARLY	RANGITATA OROGENY
150		JURASSIC		LATE	
				MIDDLE	
				EARLY	
200		TRIASSIC		LATE	
				MIDDLE	
				EARLY	DEPOSITIONAL PHASE
250	PALEOZOIC	PERMIAN		LATE	
				MIDDLE	
				EARLY	
300		CARBONIFEROUS		LATE	
				MIDDLE	
				EARLY	TUHUA OROGENY
350		DEVONIAN		LATE	
				MIDDLE	
400				EARLY	
		SILURIAN			
450		ORDOVICIAN		LATE	
				EARLY	DEPOSITIONAL PHASE
500		CAMBRIAN		LATE	
				MIDDLE	
550				EARLY	
600		PRECAMBRIAN			?

Table 1   Geological time scale

ing may occur and form very extensive troughs in the sea bed and upper layers of the crust called geosynclines, in which many thousands of metres of sediments can accumulate. The high temperature and pressure deep within the sedimentary pile can cause metamorphism. In contrast, slight downwarping allows the sea to extend over the land, producing shallow shelves close to the land and deeper basins further offshore. When compression forces the crust and overlying sediments upward, mountain chains are formed often accompanied by severe folding and fracturing of the rocks and intrusion of magma. The effect of mountain building (orogeny) varies from place to place, and locally the rocks may be only gently tilted.

Geological time scale
and its relation to New Zealand

The geological time scale which is used worldwide divides the last 600 million years up into 11 periods of differing lengths of time (Table 1). The time scale was originally established on the rock sequences of Europe. Obvious breaks in sedimentation or change in rock type marked the limits of the periods. Unfortunately these breaks and changes have not proved to occur worldwide, and it is sometimes difficult to apply the scale away from Europe. One way of correlating rock ages is to use the fossils contained within rock units. This is reasonably satisfactory as long as the animal or plant groups achieved a worldwide distribution. However, many groups did not, particularly if they preferred a particular climate or environment. Also some groups were in existence for such a long time that they cannot be used to characterise one particular geological period.

Another method of dating rocks is isotopic, where an analysis is made of the proportions of particular isotopes of elements present in the minerals comprising the rocks. Certain elements which constitute a part of some minerals begin to decay radioactively as soon as the mineral crystallises, slowly changing their isotopic character. The decay rate can be ascertained experimentally. By measuring the amount of the original and resultant elements and isotopes, and then applying the decay rate, the age of the rock can be calculated. This method is generally applied to igneous or metamorphic rocks, and even then may not be accurate if the rocks have undergone heating and deformation subsequent to their formation. Another way of estimating geological time is to apply known rates of present-day sedimentation to the thickness of rock sequences.

It can be seen from the above that there is no way of absolutely relating all New Zealand rocks to the international time scale, as the age is based on inference from global correlations, or from the relationship of one set of rocks to another whose age is known. The isolated position of New Zealand has made correlation with other parts of the world difficult, while limited laboratory resources has meant that only a small number of isotopically determined ages are available. Thus the assignment of many New Zealand rocks to the international time scale is in many instances a "best guess" and is constantly under review.

Outline of geological history

Distribution of land and sea has varied greatly during the geological past. Figure 1 illustrates the disposition of present-day crustal plates, but millions of years ago their relative positions and shapes were quite different. Some hundreds of millions of years ago a supercontinent (Gondwanaland), which included the present-day continents of South America, Africa, Australia, India, and Antarctica, existed in the southern hemisphere surrounded by sea. The New Zealand area was situated on the edge of Gondwanaland. Since that time, movements from within the earth have caused the constituent continents to break away from one another and move to their present positions— a process which is still continuing. The original supercontinent was not stationary, it too responded to forces from within the earth so that it was in different positions with respect to the earth's poles at different times. Thus at various times the fossil record and the rocks may show evidence of either cold, temperate, or tropical climate.

Evidence from the fossil record within the older rocks in New Zealand, and their composition, demonstrates their affinity with rocks of Australia and Antarctica of similar age. The relationship appears to end between 100 and 80 million years ago when New Zealand broke away from Gondwanaland and started movement toward its present position, with the accompanying formation of the Tasman Sea. Since that time New Zealand has had its own geological history and developed a unique flora and fauna.

The very oldest sedimentary rocks in New Zealand were deposited in basins lying offshore from the landmass of Gondwanaland. Subsequently the sediments were disrupted by earth movements and pushed up to form land that eventually became parts of Australia, Antarctica, and New Zealand. Later, an extensive series of depositional troughs developed offshore, which collected sediment eroded from adjacent continents for nearly two hundred million years. These are collectively known as the New Zealand Geosyncline, and were the "birthplace" of the "greywacke" rocks that now form the main ranges of New Zealand.

The era of the New Zealand Geosyncline came to a close about 110–120 million years ago when major earth movements uplifted the sediments to form new land. A period of quiescence followed when erosion reduced much of the mountainous land to a low-lying, almost level plain. It was during this time that the split between Australia and New Zealand occurred.

As the land was reduced in height, low-lying swampy areas developed, which are now the sites of major coalfields. Eventually the sea started to cover the land, firstly depositing sediments in marginal basins, and later over most of the New Zealand area. Then, about 15 million years ago, the mainly quiet period ended, and New Zealand once again suffered the onslaught of tectonic activity and consequent mountain building; volcanic activity was widespread, and earthquakes common. Through movements at different times in different places a continuing succession of isolated basins developed, filled with sediment, and were uplifted as land. In more recent geological times, the effect of rises and falls of sea level, due to glaciations and warmer intervals, were superimposed on the tectonic events.

It must be remembered that New Zealand is still involved in a continuing cycle of geological events, and the level of tectonic activity remains high. Offshore basins receiving sediment will, one day in the future, become land, while other areas onshore, being depressed, will be invaded by the sea. Our great mountains are being continually eroded— just look at the debris on their flanks (Fig. 12) and in the river valleys. Each major earthquake has an effect on the land; in 1855 the coastline of Wellington Harbour was uplifted 1.5 metres. Nothing is permanent in terms of geological time.

Figure 12   Severe erosion on the slopes of Tapuaenuku in the Inland Kaikoura Range.
Photo: D.L. Homer

Geological map of New Zealand 1 : 2 000 000

The geological map that accompanies this booklet shows the current distribution of rock units of a particular age. This distribution is not necessarily the same as it was when the rocks were originally deposited. Subsequent tectonic events may have warped and broken the rocks, so that originally contiguous deposits may have been dislocated and moved far from each other. Similarly rocks from one environment may have been brought adjacent to rocks from a very different one. What may have been a very extensive area of deposition may now be only represented by small isolated areas, the rest having been removed by erosion. The rocks mapped are those that are present at the surface— extensive sequences may be concealed and buried by younger rocks.

Sedimentary rocks on the map are distinguished on their age and not on their composition, except for the Quaternary sediments where their composition and mode of origin are also indicated. The igneous and metamorphic rocks are shown as a combination of rock type and age. These methods have been chosen, for ease of presentation on a map of this scale. At the small scale of this map, it has not been possible to show all the individual areas; a great deal of lumping

and generalisation of units has been necessary. If more information about particular areas is required, larger scale geological maps (available from the New Zealand Geological Survey) should be consulted. At larger scales there is a more detailed depiction of the geology, and more information about the rock types. Indeed, most large scale maps show rocks in "formations"— units which are defined by both rock type and age.

Several geological maps have been published at about the scale of 1 : 2 000 000. The first, in 1865, is superficially amazingly like the present map, the broad patterns of New Zealand geology already having been established at that date. In detail, however, there are wide differences between this map, that first one, and subsequent publications. The differences result mainly from increased geological knowledge as more of the country has been mapped in detail, and from refinements to the time scale. Another reason for differences is the application of "geological licence". Small areas of rock may have to be exaggerated in size at the expense of other units in order to be shown on the map; the emphasis is at the author's discretion.

Stratigraphy

Introduction

Stratigraphy is the study of the sequence of rock layers in any one area. These are generally described from the oldest to the youngest. Thus the geological legend on the map shows the ages of the rocks in this order. Against each age is a summary of the major rock types, subdivided into sedimentary and volcanic categories. The following sections (in stratigraphic order) describe where rocks belonging to a particular age are found, what sort of rocks they are, what environment they were deposited or formed in, and what has happened to them since they were first formed (deformation).

The information on age, environment of deposition or mode of formation comes from the rocks themselves or their relationships to one another. It is worthwhile briefly discussing in very general terms what forms this information takes.

Fossils can tell us much about the environment in which sedimentary rocks were deposited, as well as providing age information; certain animal groups preferred fresh, brackish, or salt water, some groups lived in deep water, some in shallow, some liked warm conditions and some cold. The environment can also be indicated by the type of deposit. As rivers carry material into the sea and lose momentum they tend to drop the coarse fractions of their load first; therefore, near-shore deposits tend to be gravel and sand, while mud is deposited further offshore. However, sea-bottom currents can move material around, and the coarseness of the material carried depends on their strength. Current and wave action may form distinctive structures which are preserved in rock. For example ripple marks in sand, as are seen on any present-day beach below high water mark, are commonly seen preserved in ancient rocks (Fig. 13) and may well indicate a shallow water environment.

The type of sediment deposited in the sea can indicate what is happening on the adjacent land area. If the land area is undergoing uplift and fast erosion

Figure 13 Ripple marks on a sandstone bed of Permian age, near Nelson. Joints cross the bed almost at right angles.   *Photo: D.L. Homer*

there will be a large amount of gravel carried out to sea. Landscapes wearing away gradually contribute more sand and mud particles. The distance that particles making up the rock have travelled is indicated by their roundness. When particles are originally eroded they are angular in shape, but as they are carried along in rivers or sea currents the particles knock against one another and gradually the corners are worn off leaving a rounded surface.

Deposits on land include angular talus debris (scree slopes), lake sediments (usually fine grained sand and mud), river deposits (intermixed layers of sand and gravel) and swamp deposits. Terrestrial deposits can be economically important, for swamps and deltas are generally full of dead and rotting vegetation, and depending on events after deposition this carbonaceous material can become coal, or the source of oil or natural gas.

Igneous rock does not give many clues as to the type of environment it was formed in. Plutonic rocks can be intruded into hard rocks on land or softer deposits beneath the sea. In general, intrusion of plutonic rocks accompanies mountain building activities. A relative age can be estimated from the rocks intruded. If the rocks in contact with the intrusion show alteration in the form of an aureole, they have been "baked" by the heat of the magma and are thus older than the intrusion. On the other hand, rocks which are in sedimentary contact with an intrusion and which show no alteration are younger than the intrusion.

Volcanoes, by their very nature, erupt intermittently. Therefore, lava flows may be interbedded with sediments, so that the fossils within the sediments can be used to date the volcanicity. Volcanoes may erupt beneath the sea or on land, and the form of the lava can indicate this. Molten lava is chilled rapidly when it meets the sea, so that a skin is formed quickly; this skin takes the form of a sack or pillow which is filled with lava. Thus the outside edge of the "pillow" is fine grained while the centre, which cooled slowly, is coarser grained and has radial cooling cracks (Fig. 14). Lava flows erupted on land are exposed to erosion and alteration by weathering; thus a weathered layer may be present between two flows. Volcanic ash falling to the ground, into the sea, or a lake, will form a bedded deposit, and is called tuff. The age of the tuff beds can be determined by their relationship with fossiliferous sediments, or by isotopic dating.

Metamorphism takes place after the rocks have been formed, and isotopic methods are used to determine the date of formation of the metamorphic minerals. Some rocks, however, may have undergone several periods of metamorphism which make them very difficult to date, as the assessed date will nearly always be the last event. Slightly metamorphosed rocks may show enough of the character of, and relationship to the parent rock that their age can be assessed.

Precambrian   *n*

Distribution   The only known Precambrian rocks occur in a small area on the west coast of the South Island near Charleston (Fig. 15). It is suspected that rocks of Precambrian age also exist in Fiordland.

18

Content   Gneiss (Fig. 16) and granite near Charleston have been dated at about 680 million years. Gneiss in Fiordland mapped as granulite facies has not been dated, and may possibly be of Precambrian age because similar rocks in other countries have proved to be that age. However, there is no supporting evidence from the New Zealand rocks.*

Paleogeographic conditions   These very old rocks would originally have been part of Gondwanaland, the landmass from which lower† Paleozoic sediments were eroded.

Comment   Previous geological maps of New Zealand have shown large areas of sandstone and argillite rocks on the west coast of the South Island to be of Precambrian age. However, Ordovician fossils were found recently in these rocks near Reefton, and it is now thought likely that the rocks range from Cambrian to Ordovician in age.

Cambrian   C, *C*

Distribution   Cambrian rocks are certainly known only from the northwest of the South Island, between the Aorere River and Maruia Springs (see Fig. 15). Cambrian rocks also almost certainly exist in Fiordland, but have not been identified as such.

Content   In Northwest Nelson the rock types are very varied, with slate, argillite, chert, hard sandstone, limestone lenses, and widespread conglomerate (Fig. 17), all being of sedimentary origin, while basalt, andesite, and tuff are representative of widespread volcanic activity. In the upper Takaka River, a layered igneous complex of serpentinised peridotite, gabbro, and diorite was intruded at this time but is too small to show on this map. Most of the rocks are metamorphosed to a greater or lesser extent, in particular the volcanics, but in most places the parent rocks can be recognised. In Fiordland, probable Cambrian rocks include schist and gneiss.

Paleogeographic conditions   The sediments were deposited in a shallow marine environment on the flanks of a volcanic arc, offshore from Gondwanaland. The widespread conglomerate formation represents a deltaic fan. At this time the Fiordland area lay close to Northwest Nelson and it is likely similar conditions prevailed.

Deformation   All the Cambrian rocks are complexly deformed by several phases of deformation. In particular large scale thrusting of "loops" of sediment many kilometres from their original site is evident. Tight folding and shearing of sediments is common.

---

* Recent (1985) isotopic dating of these rocks has shown them to be of Cretaceous age. Also, they are interpreted as intruding the older amphibolite facies gneiss.

† The terms lower, middle, and upper refer to the position within the body of rock, while the terms early, middle, and late refer to the time of deposition or emplacement.

Figure 14 Pillow lava overlying mudstone at Muriwai Beach, near Auckland. Note the distinct rim of each pillow and the radial jointing formed as each molten pillow solidifies. Largest pillows about 1 m across.

Photo: S.N. Beatus

Ordovician O

Distribution Ordovician rocks are widespread throughout the western South Island (see Fig. 15). They are also known from southern Fiordland and Stewart Island.

Content Limestone and marble are characteristic of the Ordovician in Northwest Nelson, with the marble being particularly well exposed on Takaka Hill (Fig. 18). Hard sandstone, argillite, black shale, and white quartzite bands occur mainly to the west of the limestone. Many of these lithologies are metamorphosed to some degree. Alternating hard sandstone and argillite are present in areas south of Northwest Nelson as far as Milford Sound, and similar rocks occur at Preservation Inlet with Ordovician fossils. Some schists and gneisses are likely to be of Ordovician age in Fiordland, as is schist surrounded by granite in Stewart Island.

Paleogeographic conditions The sandstone and argillite were deposited in a fairly deep trough lying off-shore from Gondwanaland, while the limestone was deposited on the Cambrian volcanic chain which had become extinct.

Deformation The Ordovician rocks in Northwest Nelson are complexly deformed and some were also involved in the major thrusting which affected Cambrian rocks (Fig. 19). The Ordovician rocks further south are not as complexly deformed, but tend to be steeply dipping and in places tightly folded.

Silurian–Devonian D

Rocks of these ages are mapped together because their individual outcrop areas are too small to be shown at the map scale.

Distribution Silurian rocks occur only in Northwest Nelson whereas Devonian rocks are present close to the Silurian rocks as well as further south near Reefton (see Fig. 15). It is likely that rocks of these two

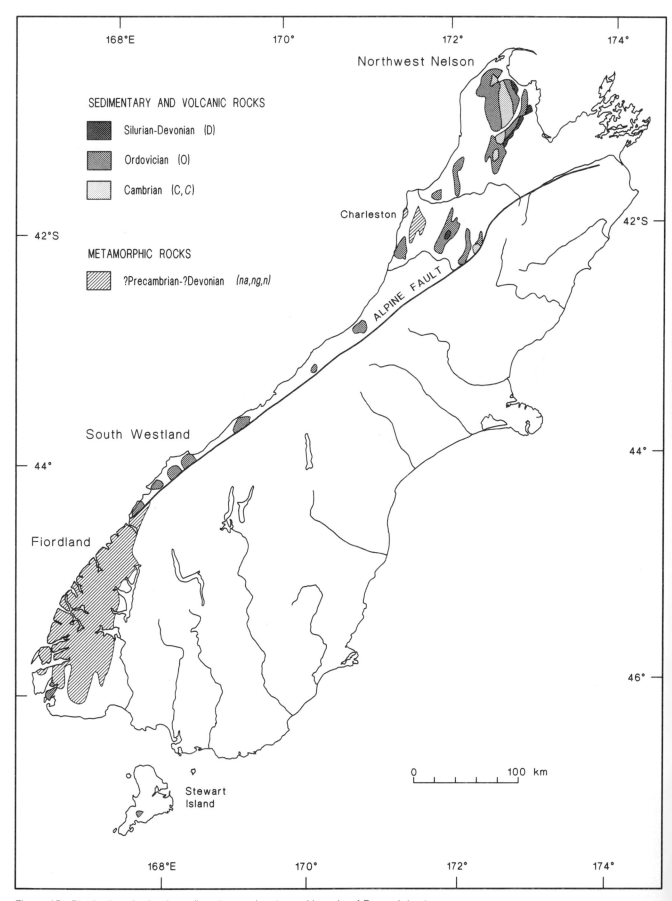

Figure 15 Distribution of volcanic, sedimentary, and metamorphic rocks of Precambrian to Devonian age.

Figure 16 Gneiss of Precambrian age, showing distinct quartz banding, on the coast near Charleston.   *Photo: T.R. Ulyatt*

Figure 17 Lockett Conglomerate of Cambrian age near Cobb River in Northwest Nelson. Both igneous and sedimentary boulders make up the conglomerate, and the matrix is coarse sandstone. Numerous joints may be seen passing through matrix and boulders.   *Photo: L. Laronde*

Figure 18 Typical karst topography developed on Ordovician marble on Takaka Hill, Northwest
Nelson   *N.Z.G.S. photo*

Figure 19 Mount Patriarch in Northwest Nelson. Ordovician limestone is involved in a major thrust
through the top of this peak. The position of the thrust (solid line with triangles) and the fold in the
beds above (dashed lines) is marked.   *N.Z.G.S. photo*

Figure 20 Well bedded quartzite of Ordovician age by the Cobb River in Northwest Nelson.
Bedding planes dip gently into the rock face; numerous, almost vertical joints are also visible.

N.Z.G.S. photo

periods occur in Fiordland. Many igneous intrusions in the west and south of the South Island are mainly of Devonian age.

Content Silurian rocks are dominantly quartzite (Fig. 20), with minor argillite and limestone, and metamorphic equivalents. Until the late 1960s it was uncertain that rocks of Silurian age existed in New Zealand, but then the quartzites yielded Silurian fossils. Schist, penetrated in the Moa-1b oil well north west of Cape Egmont, has been correlated with similar rocks of Silurian age in Northwest Nelson.

Devonian rocks are more varied, with calcareous mudstone, sandstone, and conglomerate in the Northwest Nelson area, but near Reefton quartzite, limestone, and mudstone are the dominant rock types.

Some schists and gneisses in Fiordland are likely to have formed by metamorphism during this period. Large granite and granodiorite intrusions occurred in the Devonian, mainly as the Karamea Batholith in the northwest of the South Island, and also as smaller discrete intrusions further south. South of Riwaka in Northwest Nelson a basic complex of gabbro, peridotite, and diorite is of Devonian age. In Fiordland and Stewart Island are large intrusions of granite and diorite.

Paleogeographic conditions The Silurian and Devonian sedimentary rocks were the final deposits of the offshore trough which had existed throughout the early Paleozoic. Crustal movements generated magma which penetrated the sedimentary pile, and eventually

23

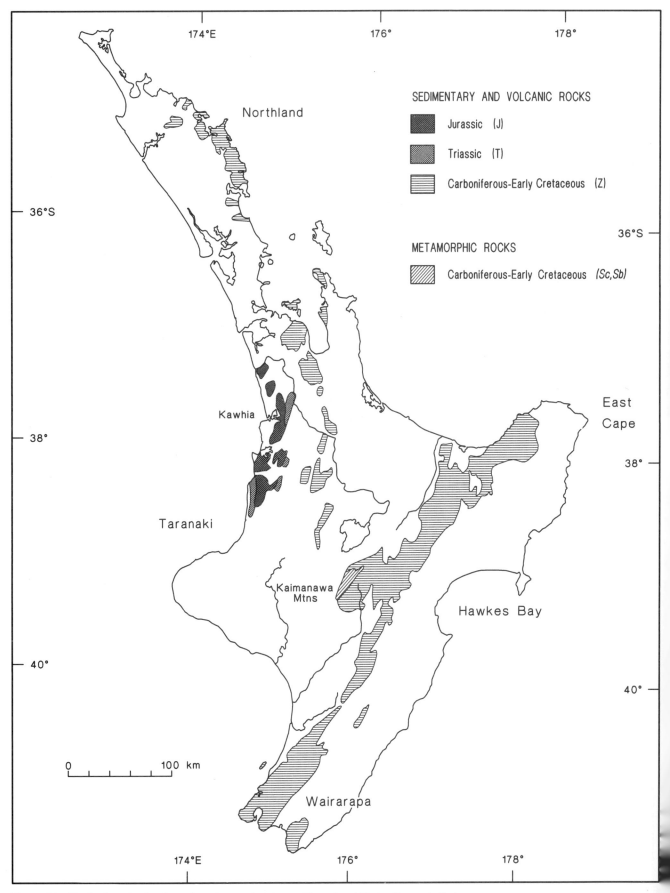

Figure 21 Distribution of volcanic, sedimentary, and metamorphic rocks of Carboniferous to Early Cretaceous age.

24

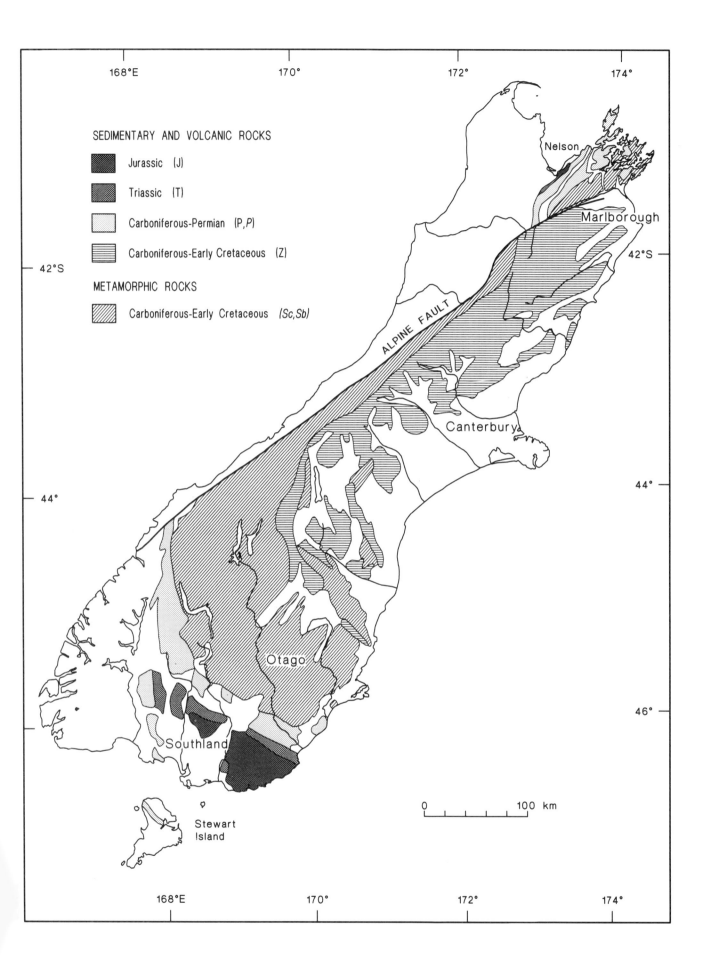

SEDIMENTARY AND VOLCANIC ROCKS

- Jurassic (J)
- Triassic (T)
- Carboniferous-Permian (P,P)
- Carboniferous-Early Cretaceous (Z)

METAMORPHIC ROCKS

- Carboniferous-Early Cretaceous (Sc,Sb)

Nelson

Marlborough

ALPINE FAULT

Canterbury

Otago

Southland

Stewart
Island

0   100 km

Figure 22 Evenly bedded, steeply dipping coarse sandstone of Permian age, near Nelson. Note slight variations in dip, and minor fault crossing outcrop on left.   Photo: D.L. Homer

cooled to become the large batholiths of granite, granodiorite, and diorite. The resulting pressure and heat were responsible for much of the metamorphism of the lower Paleozoic rocks.

Deformation The crustal movements in the Devonian (and continuing intermittently through to the Permian— Tuhua Orogeny) were largely responsible for the deformation of the lower Paleozoic rocks. On the whole, the Silurian and Devonian rocks were not involved in the earlier major thrusting events, but they are faulted and tightly folded.

Carboniferous–Early Cretaceous

Introduction The rocks of these ages are shown on the map in two different columns: one which divides the rocks into separate ages, and another which shows the entire age range undivided. On examining the distribution of these groups on the map it will be seen that the first group lies invariably to the west or south of the second group (see also Fig. 21). The legend description also shows the rocks of the first group to be far more varied. The age information derived from the rocks of the first group is plentiful and distinctive, whereas it has proved very difficult to differentiate the second group on either age or lithology. These rocks

are therefore discussed under headings equivalent to those units shown on the map legend.

Carboniferous–Permian P, *P*
There is no fossil evidence of Carboniferous age from rocks in this map unit, but because thick sequences of unfossiliferous rocks underlie rocks of known Permian age, they are thought to range down into the Carboniferous. The only known Carboniferous fossil locality exists in rocks described below in the section "Carboniferous–Early Cretaceous".

Distribution Sedimentary rocks of Permian* age are present in the north of the South Island and in a broad band extending from northwestern Otago through Southland to the east coast, south of Dunedin (Fig. 21). Igneous rocks have a similar distribution. It is thought probable that Permian rocks exist offshore to the west of Kawhia and Taranaki.

Content The Permian sedimentary rocks are characterised by a very high content of volcanic-derived fragments (volcanogenic), but are otherwise very variable. The sediments in the Nelson area vary from fossiliferous conglomerate, sandstone (Fig. 22), mud-

---

* Fossils of Triassic age have been found within these rocks on the coast south of Dunedin.

26

Figure 23   Aerial view of Dun Mountain (unvegetated light coloured area in the centre) with the Permian melange belt at the left exhibiting typical hummocky topography.   Photo: D.L. Homer

stone, and limestone in the west to more sparsely fossiliferous, slightly metamorphosed sandstone and mudstone with rare limestone and conglomerate in the east. The western sequence commonly contains interbedded tuff and more rarely bands of basalt. A very similar sequence occurs in northwestern Otago and northern Southland, with the fossiliferous rocks to the west or south of the slightly metamorphosed sequence.

Volcanic rocks are intimately associated with sedimentary rocks in both the Nelson and Southland regions, although they are more prominent in the south where they form the bulk of the Takitimu Mountains and extend in a thin band north through the Eglinton and Hollyford valleys. The volcanics comprise basalt, andesite, porphyry and keratophyre, volcanic breccia, tuff, and minor interbedded sediments. The volcanic band is not differentiated on the map in the Nelson region because of scale problems.

The Permian is also represented by an association of rocks known as an ophiolite assemblage, composed of deep water sediment, submarine basalt, and very basic plutonic rocks occurring in long narrow belts. It is thought that these rocks represent a slice of sea floor that made up an old subduction zone. The Permian ophiolite assemblages are recognised in Nelson and northwestern Otago. In Nelson the plutonic

rocks comprise gabbro, dunite (named from Dun Mountain, see Fig. 23), peridotite, and serpentinite. In this area some parts of the original layered plutonic complex have been deformed by later tectonic events so as to break up into large blocks in a chaotic manner. This chaotic mass is called a melange (Fig. 23) and is characterised by the widespread occurrence of serpentine. The melange belt extends to the north and south of the recognised ophiolite sequence of the Dun Mountain–Red Hills area. In northwestern Otago the ophiolite assemblage is best seen at Red Mountain which is composed of peridotite, dunite, and serpentinite, and extends south and east in a belt.

The basic plutonic complexes of the Longwood Range, Bluff, and Lake Rotoroa are also thought to be of Permian age. These comprise gabbro and peridotite as the main rock types, and are probably associated with the volcanics of the Takitimu Mountains and Nelson. The Longwood and Lake Rotoroa complexes are intruded by later granitic phases.

At Parapara Peak, Northwest Nelson, is an important occurrence of freshwater and shallow marine rocks which have no volcanic content. This sequence is too small to show on the map.

Paleogeographic conditions Following the events of the Tuhua Orogeny, which formed new continental

Figure 24 Triassic conglomerate forming cliffs at Tapirimoko Point, south of Kawhia. Dip is towards left of photo. *Photo: D.L. Homer*

crust on the edge of Gondwanaland, a volcanic arc developed offshore. To the east of the arc a major sedimentary basin began to develop which would become the New Zealand Geosyncline. The Carboniferous–Permian rocks were mainly deposited on the edges of the geosyncline and close to the volcanic arc. The rocks of eastern Nelson and northern Southland with a lesser volcanic content were deposited in deeper water and further from the arc. A subduction zone east of the continental margin was actively subducting oceanic crust, causing the volcanic activity and a trench to develop above it. The "fossil" subduction zone is represented by the ophiolite belts. The small area of rocks at Parapara Peak represents deposition adjacent to the continent to the west of the subduction zone.

Deformation Some of the Permian rocks are part of a major downfold (syncline) structure also involving

the younger Triassic and Jurassic rocks in Nelson and Southland. Within the major structure the rocks are commonly tightly folded with steep dips. Locally there are areas of shearing and major faulting.

Triassic T

Distribution Triassic rocks have a similar distribution pattern to that of the Permian in the South Island (i.e., Nelson and Southland). However, they also occur in the west of the North Island, from northern Taranaki to the Waikato River (see Fig. 21).

Content The Triassic rocks are basically similar to the Permian rocks. Conglomerate (Fig. 24), sandstone, and mudstone, mainly derived from volcanic rock types, are common, while tuff beds are widespread

Figure 25   A coarse sandstone containing oyster shells sharply overlies a finer sandstone. A Jurassic rock on the Catlins coast, Southland.   *Photo: S.N. Beatus*

particularly in the North Island; volcanic flow rocks are rare. In places the rocks are very fossiliferous giving good age control.

Paleogeographic conditions   The deposits are generally of a shallow marine shelf environment west of a deeper trough. The amount of volcanic materials indicate sporadic volcanic activity continued from the Permian. The quantity of conglomerate indicates proximity to a land mass.

Deformation   The Triassic rocks are involved in the major downfolds of the Kawhia, Nelson, and Southland regional synclines. In Southland and Kawhia the rocks are not highly deformed, but in the main only gently folded. In Nelson the syncline is severely faulted.

Jurassic   J

Distribution   Jurassic rocks are widespread in Southland, are present in a small block near Pike River in northwestern Otago, and have a limited extent in Nelson. They are well represented in the west of the North Island (see Fig. 21).

Content   Mainly sandstone (Fig. 25), mudstone, and conglomerate. Tuff bands are rarer than in the Triassic sequence, and are more common in the North Island. Freshwater sandstone and conglomerate with plant fossils and minor coal seams form the Middle Jurassic beds in the South Island, but do not occur until the Late Jurassic (Fig. 26) in the North Island. Marine deposits are interbedded with the freshwater rocks in both areas.

29

Figure 26 Coarse terrestrial sandstone overlying thin coal seams (below hammer) in uppermost Jurassic beds, south of the Waikato River. Tertiary limestone overlies the sequence with slight unconformity at the top of the photo. *Photo: B.C. Waterhouse*

Paleogeographic conditions The Jurassic sediments were laid down on an ever-shallowing shelf, over which sea level oscillated so that at some times marine conditions prevailed and at others the shelf was above sea level. The response to the lower sea levels was rapid downcutting by rivers and associated influxes of gravel to the marine basins. Volcanic activity had almost ceased.

Deformation Jurassic rocks are generally gently folded and form the core of the Kawhia and Southland synclines. The Jurassic in Nelson and northern Fiordland is severely faulted.

Carboniferous–Early Cretaceous Z, *Sc, Sb*

Distribution The rocks are widely distributed throughout both islands (see Fig. 21). While sedimentary rocks dominate in the North Island and form a wide northeast–southwest-trending belt in the South Island, their metamorphic equivalents, schists, form a belt which crosses the southern part of the South Island from east to west, then curves north to trend northeast in a decreasingly narrow belt. Schist is also present locally in the Kaimanawa Mountains of the North Island and in the Chatham Islands.

Content The dominant rock types are hard grey sandstone and darker coloured mudstone (argillite). These generally form alternating sequences (Fig. 27) with the sandstone predominant, and are commonly referred to jointly as "greywacke". (In strict geological terminology only the sandstone should be called greywacke, but in this account, the word "greywacke" will be taken to mean— as it commonly is in New Zealand literature— the alternating sequence of hard sandstone and argillite.) Minor rock types found interbedded with or faulted into the "greywacke" include limestone, chert, conglomerate, spilite, and chaotic melange units.

Although the rocks of this period contain few age-diagnostic fossils there does seem to be a general pattern of age distribution. In southern Canterbury, near Geraldine, the only Carboniferous fossil locality in New Zealand is in limestone within a melange unit. Permian fossils are present in the general area including the Waitaki valley, and it appears that this area is the oldest representative of the "greywacke" type regime. Further west and north into mid Canterbury, Triassic fossils are present, while further north again into North Canterbury and Marlborough, Jurassic fossils and then Early Cretaceous plant fossils respectively occur, demonstrating a general younging trend to the north and east.

Figure 27 Typical alternating sequence of sandstone (thicker and light coloured) and mudstone, composing shore platform of "greywacke" near Wellington. Minor faults cross from left to upper right, and small-scale folds are visible at extreme top right. Probable Triassic age.

Photo: D.L. Homer

In the North Island the pattern is not so clear. The main Tararua, Ruahine, and Kaimanawa ranges appear to be mainly Triassic in age while those further north and east are younger (Jurassic and possibly Early Cretaceous). Permian fossils have been found in limestone in Northland, but Jurassic fossils are present in mudstone a little further south. It is thought that the main "greywacke" province of Northland is probably Jurassic in age and that the Permian limestone is a remnant of a different depositional regime. The Jurassic rocks of the northwestern part of the North Island are characterised by the widespread occurrence of chert horizons. "Greywacke" rocks in the east of the North

Island from Wairarapa to East Cape are mainly Jurassic in age, but like those in Marlborough could range into the Early Cretaceous. Similar rock types, but with a different deformation style and containing Early–mid Cretaceous fossils, are mapped and described separately (see Cretaceous).

Metamorphic rocks present in the South Island, the Kaimanawa Mountains, and in the Chatham Islands are considered mostly to be metamorphic equivalents of the "greywacke" and of the same age range. The boundary between "greywacke" and schist is transitional and in the less metamorphosed part of the sequence, sedimentary features can still be seen

31

Figure 28 Disrupted bedding in schist, Maerewhenua River, Central Otago. Original sandstone and mudstone beds have been folded, stretched, and compressed during metamorphism.

Photo: D.G. Bishop

that enables recognition of the "parent" rock. These sedimentary features become obliterated (Fig. 28) as the metamorphic grade increases. The sandstone and mudstone form schist with different features, with quartz bands and laminations being more common in rock derived from sandstone; metamorphosed volcanic bands become a characteristic green colour (greenschist). Most of the schist in Otago, Marlborough, and the Chatham Islands falls into the chlorite metamorphic zone (see page 12, above), which itself is divided into four textural zones which are recognisable by changes in the rock as the metamorphic grade increases. The higher grade metamorphic zones (biotite, garnet, and oligoclase) are restricted to the western parts of Otago and the Southern Alps. Two small parallel belts of chlorite zone schist are mapped in the Kaimanawa Mountains in the North Island, and it is possible more might be found when the area is mapped in detail.

Paleogeographic conditions There are two main interpretations of the paleogeography at this time:

1. The most commonly stated version is that an enormous trough or series of troughs, the New Zealand Geosyncline, developed offshore from the continental landmass of Australia (still part of Gondwanaland) at the end of Devonian and the beginning of the Carboniferous. On the edges of the geosyncline the rocks described in the previous sections (Carboniferous–Permian, Triassic, and Jurassic) were deposited, while the monotonous, thick, "greywacke" sequences collected in the main part of the geosyncline. Rocks deposited in this geosyncline are now found as far away as New Caledonia in the north, as far south as the Auckland Islands, and the Chatham Islands to the east. The geosyncline existed for a period of about 200 million years, and a huge thickness of sediments collected in it. As the sediments collected, their weight helped to warp the crust downward so that more sediments could be collected. Subsequent earth movements caused the sediments to be uplifted.

The geosyncline existed for longer in some areas than in others. In the Marlborough–East Cape region, deposition continued into the Early Cretaceous while further south and west freshwater beds and shallow marine deposits indicate marked shallowing of water and appearance of land during the Middle and latest Jurassic. In the depths of the geosyncline the sediments were metamorphosed both by pressure from the weight of the sediments above and heat from the earth's crust. Burial and compaction of sediments were also responsible for consolidation and cementation into hard rocks, while compression within the geosyncline caused fracturing (jointing) within the solid rock. Water percolating along the fractures deposited minerals resulting in the quartz, calcite, and zeolite veining commonly seen in "greywacke".

Figure 29 Hard Cretaceous sandstone forms distinctive knobbly ridges known as "taipos" in southeastern Wairarapa. *Photo: D.L. Homer*

2. The mineral content of the "greywacke" in the South Island is different from that of the western and southern Permian–Jurassic rocks described previously. Therefore, it is argued that the source of sediment supply was different too. Also there is evidence to suggest that the sediment was mostly derived from the south and east and not from the west. The alternative hypothesis for the source of the "greywacke" rocks is that they were deposited on a shelving sea floor, perhaps adjacent to the continent that would become Antarctica, where there is rock with the right type of minerals to have supplied the "greywacke". This sediment was then "rafted" by plate movement towards a subduction zone offshore from Australia, until it came into juxtaposition with the volcanic-derived suite of Permian–Jurassic rocks. The large volume of lightweight sediments could not be subducted and the resulting collision of the two plates caused the sediment to thickly pile up with consequent complexity of structure, metamorphism of the sediments, and the final mountain building episode (Rangitata Orogeny).

The "greywacke" rocks of the northern part of the North Island show a mixed mineral content and their history may have been a combination of the events described above.

Deformation The "greywacke" rocks are commonly extremely deformed (see Frontispiece, Fig. 51), fractured, and veined, and the mudstone in particular is commonly very sheared. Some deformation took place within the sedimentary pile, but the severe folding, faulting, and shearing were caused by the Rangitata Orogeny, and the rocks were further deformed by the later Kaikoura Orogeny. In many areas it is difficult to see original sedimentary features because of severe deformation.

Cretaceous K, *K*

Distribution Cretaceous sedimentary rocks are widespread, but are exposed only at the surface in isolated patches, the largest being in Northland, East Cape, Wairarapa (Fig. 29), and Marlborough (Fig. 30). Significant smaller areas are near Collingwood, Greymouth, Dunedin, and in the Chatham Islands. A feature of Cretaceous time was igneous activity, and granite occurs in many places in the South Island, while volcanic rocks are widespread in Northland, East Cape, Marlborough, parts of Canterbury, and the Chatham Islands.

33

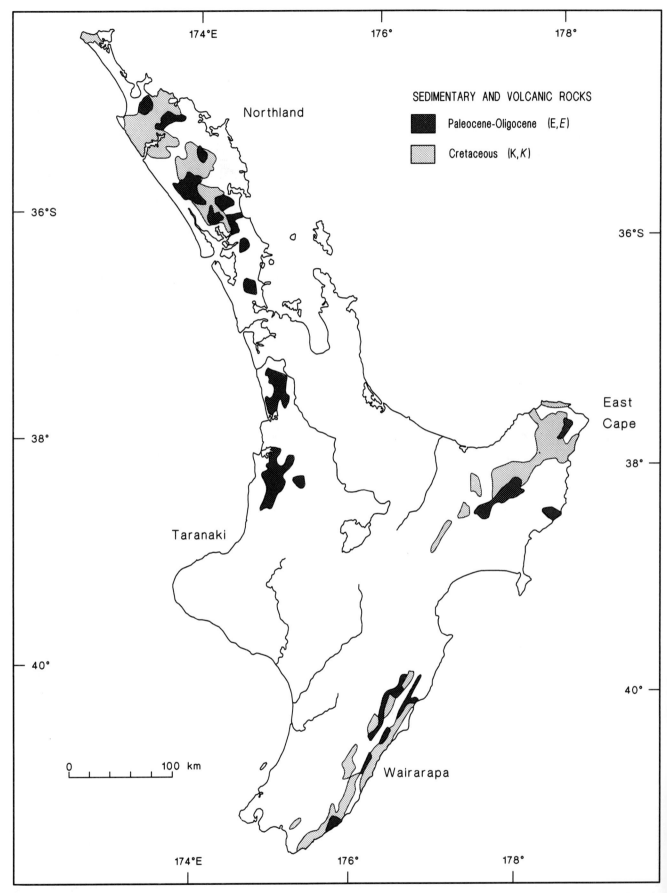

Figure 30   Distribution of volcanic and sedimentary rocks of Cretaceous to Oligocene age.

34

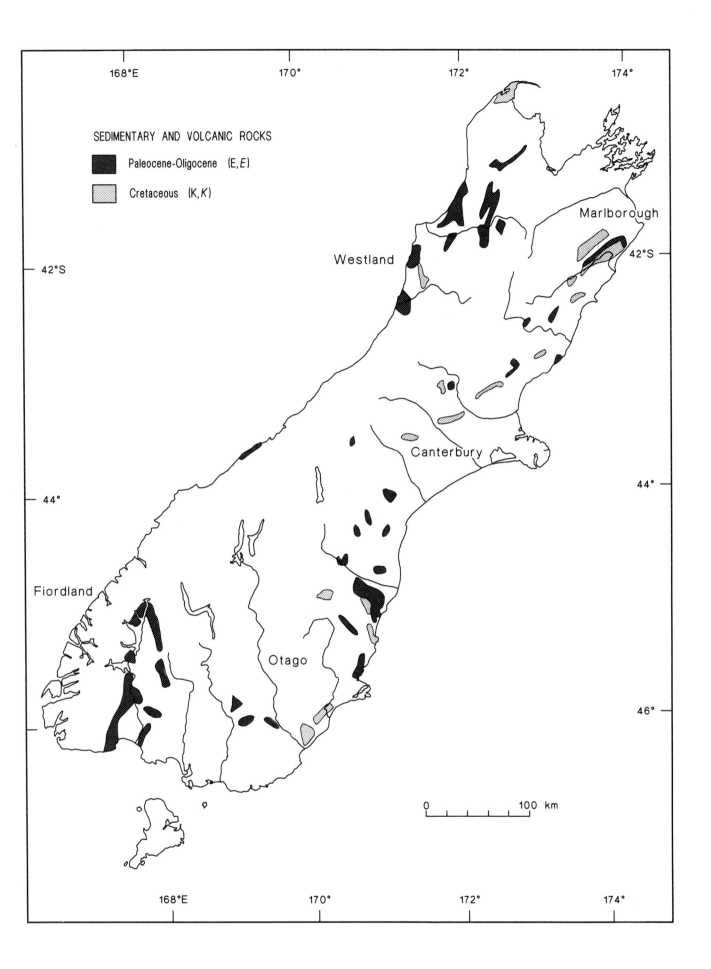

SEDIMENTARY AND VOLCANIC ROCKS

▮ Paleocene-Oligocene (E,*E*)

▦ Cretaceous (K,*K*)

Marlborough

Westland

Canterbury

Fiordland

Otago

168°E   170°   172°   174°

42°S

44°

46°

0   100 km

35

Figure 31 Mid Cretaceous terrestrial breccia in the Buller Gorge. The breccia is composed of angular fragments of varying sizes and lithologies; bedding is shown by the lens of fine sediment at lower left. The breccia is intruded by an igneous dike (vertical) of later Cretaceous age, which exhibits contact metamorphism on both sides (whiter zones). *Photo: B.D. Scott*

Content The Cretaceous was a time of widely differing depositional environments resulting in varied rock types. There appears to be a gap in the fossil record spanning the earliest Cretaceous, so that knowledge of this time is limited. It seems likely that in the Marlborough, Wairarapa, and East Cape regions the regime of the New Zealand Geosyncline continued and in some "greywacke" rocks in Marlborough, plant fossils of late Early Cretaceous time have been found. These rocks are shown as Z on the map and described in the previous section.

Marine fossils of Early–mid Cretaceous age have been found in Marlborough, Wairarapa, and East Cape. These rocks, although similar in appearance to the bulk of the "greywacke" (i.e., sandstone and mudstone), are actually softer and deformed quite differently, with slump folds and internal folding indicating

deformation while the rocks were still soft. Other rocks of mid Cretaceous age in Northland, East Cape, Wairarapa, and Marlborough are undeformed alternating sandstone and mudstone with rare chert, limestone, and spilite beds. Towards the end of the Cretaceous these areas were probably locally briefly emergent, but by the end of the Cretaceous there was a return to marine conditions, and the common sediments deposited then were sandstone, commonly glauconitic (greensand), and siliceous mudstone.

Although the Cretaceous rocks are dominantly marine in the North Island and the northeast of the South Island, the rocks in the rest of the South Island are mainly of terrestrial origin. Areas of coarse conglomerate and breccia occur in Westland (Fig. 31) and in Central Otago, and are of mid Cretaceous age. Terrestrial sand and conglomerate of similar age occurs

Figure 32 Unvegetated "tops" of the Paparoa Range expose granite of Cretaceous age.

Photo: D.L. Homer

at Puysegur Point in southern Fiordland. In the coastal areas and in inland Canterbury coal measures and terrestrial sand and mud are of Late Cretaceous age. Some of New Zealand's biggest coal mines are in these Cretaceous rocks, particularly near Greymouth, but also at Kaitangata, Ohai, and Collingwood. Nonmarine deposits of mid to Late Cretaceous age are present on Pitt Island in the Chathams.

Igneous activity was rife in the Cretaceous. Large areas of granite at Separation Point, the west of the South Island, Fiordland, and Stewart Island were intruded during the mid Cretaceous (Fig. 32). Granite was intruded into older igneous complexes such as those at Lake Rotoroa and Longwood Range, causing reheating of rocks and the formation of metamorphic aureoles and hybrid rocks by the assimilation of chunks of old solid rock into the molten magma. Aureoles are also common in sediments. The plutonic activity was mainly acid except in Marlborough where a basic layered complex of gabbro and diorite in association with extensive dolerite dike intrusion forms Tapuaenuku (see Fig. 12) and surroundings in the Inland Kaikoura Range. Basalt rocks nearby are the extrusive phase of activity. Further south in mid Canterbury, rhyolite and dacite are present at Mt Somers

and the Malvern Hills together with minor andesite. Basalt and marine tuff are present on the Chatham Islands.

In the North Island, volcanic activity was widespread in Northland and East Cape where basalt (with pillow form) and minor keratophyre are interbedded with sediments. (This activity almost certainly continued into the Eocene, particularly in East Cape.) A small gabbroic intrusion associated with serpentine occurs at North Cape and other isolated small dioritic bodies are present in Northland.

Paleogeographic conditions The Cretaceous was a time of great environmental change. At the beginning of the Cretaceous came the climax of the mountain building phase of the Rangitata Orogeny and the widespread igneous activity associated with it. Thus the New Zealand area was mainly a mountainous landmass, especially in the southern and western areas. A trough still existed in the east, however, and marine deposition continued (Fig. 33). The stirrings of the crust were reflected in the deformation of these soft sediments. As conditions became more stable, the mountainous land was eroded virtually to a flat plain.

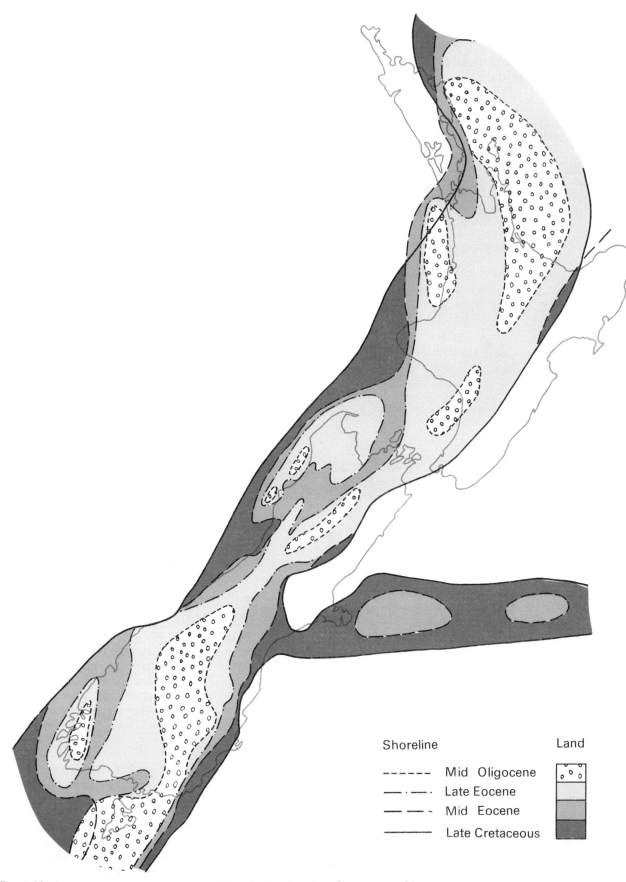

Shoreline

------- Mid Oligocene

—·—·— Late Eocene

— — — Mid Eocene

——— Late Cretaceous

Land

Figure 33   Diagram showing paleogeography of New Zealand from Late Cretaceous to Oligocene time. Note the progressive reduction in land area as the sea invaded.

Rapid erosion is indicated by the thick breccia deposits of Central Otago and south of the Buller River. Swampy plains developed at the coastal margins and in low-lying areas, collecting and preserving dead vegetation that would eventually become coal. Finally at the end of the Cretaceous coastal areas were invaded by the sea, especially in the east, and marine conditions again prevailed.

A major event late in the Cretaceous was the gradual splitting off of the New Zealand area from Australia. A spreading ridge developed in the area that was to become the Tasman Sea; this ended New Zealand's long association with the Australian continent, and from the Late Cretaceous New Zealand has had independent geological, faunal, and floral development.

Deformation The Rangitata Orogeny continued in the Early Cretaceous and deformed earlier rocks and accumulating marine sediments. However, the later part of the Cretaceous was generally a quiet time, and many Cretaceous rocks are not severely deformed. Later tilting, folding, and faulting associated with the Kaikoura Orogeny is responsible for most deformation seen.

Paleocene–Eocene–Oligocene E, *E*

Rocks of these ages are mapped together solely for cartographic convenience. In some places the areas are so tiny it is impossible to show them individually, but in other places rocks of each age unit may cover a large area which could easily be shown. Overall it is simpler to map rocks of these ages as a unit. However, the deposits of each epoch and their paleoenvironments are quite distinct.

Distribution Paleocene rocks crop out in Marlborough, Canterbury, on the west coast of the South Island, east coast of the North Island, and in Northland. Eocene rocks follow a similar pattern, but are more widespread. Oligocene rocks are most widespread in the northwest of the South Island, the north and west of the North Island and in Southland and Otago (see Fig. 30). Rocks of this age grouping are also found on outlying islands. The Paleocene–Eocene rocks are concealed by younger deposits in many areas, particularly in the west of the North Island, but Oligocene deposits, which once covered much of the country, have been subsequently largely removed by erosion.

Figure 34 Symmetrical anticline in limestone of Eocene age, plunges away from the viewer. White Rock, southern Wairarapa.   *N.Z.G.S. photo*

Figure 35 Bentonitic mudstone is very prone to slumping and this coastal landslide near Porangahau, Wairarapa is typical.   *Photo: D.L. Homer*

Content The rocks are mainly sedimentary, the few volcanic rocks being confined to the South Island and Chatham Islands where basalt and tuff are found in mid and South Canterbury, South Westland, and on the main Chatham Island.

The Paleocene is represented by marine greensand, siliceous mudstone and chert, minor limestone, and sandstone in the east of both islands, Northland, and Chatham Island. In South Westland, however, marine conglomerate, greensand, and limestone date from this time.

The Eocene rocks are also dominantly of marine origin in the east of both islands: glauconitic sandstone is still common, while a distinctive white limestone is present in North Canterbury, Marlborough, and southern Wairarapa (Fig. 34). Bentonitic mudstone (Fig. 35) is a characteristic deposit of areas in Wairarapa, Hawkes Bay, and some areas of Northland. An unusual deposit dating from the Eocene is the Oamaru Diatomite, a siliceous mudstone made up entirely of the hard parts of tiny marine organisms called diatoms. The western and southern areas of the South Island and western areas of the North Island all contain non-marine deposits of Eocene age; many

of these are coal measure deposits (Fig. 36) with seams of bituminous and sub-bituminous coal. Although not obvious from the map, Eocene deposits are widespread in the west of the North Island, but are concealed by younger rocks. Eocene coal measures are present at depth, and have been found in drillholes (e.g., Kapuni), from Taranaki north to the Waikato River. Coal measures near Whangarei in Northland date from the Late Eocene. In the Late Eocene, marine deposits of mudstone, greensand, and limestone are recorded from areas in the south of the South Island.

Oligocene deposits are almost entirely of marine origin and are characterised by limestone or other calcareous sediments. In the Te Kuiti area of the North Island, limestone is widespread and there is extensive cave development (e.g., Waitomo, Fig. 37) and karst topography. Calcareous sandstone and mudstone are also present in this area. In Northland, limestone is the predominant rock type of this age, whereas glauconitic sandstone, mudstone, and minor limestone are more common on the east coast of the North Island, Marlborough, and North Canterbury. Limestone is again widely developed in the west of the South Island as well as calcareous mudstone, as it is in South Can-

Figure 36   Abandoned mine in Eocene coal measures south of Charleston. The coal seam which is excavated, is overlain by carbonaceous muddy sandstone in turn overlain by white quartz sand at the top.   *Photo: D.L. Homer*

terbury and Otago, but here a high glauconitic content is typical. Near Lake Wakatipu small slivers of limestone and glauconitic sandstone are preserved indicating the original wide extent of marine deposition in the Oligocene. Even so, some areas of Central Otago and Southland were above sea level and have terrestrial deposits of coal measures dating from this time extending into the Miocene, and the lignite resources in these deposits are very extensive.

Paleogeographic conditions   At the end of the Cretaceous much of the mountainous land had been eroded to an almost-level plain, though the process continued well into the Eocene in western and southern districts.

The land mass was very low at this time and deeply weathered; coal measures were being deposited in the swampy, marginal coastal area. The Paleocene and Eocene saw a gradual invasion of the land by the sea (see Fig. 33), particularly in the east. By the Late Eocene only the western half of the North Island and a belt of land with offshore islands further south existed above sea level. The sea continued its invasion in the Oligocene until the New Zealand area was almost entirely submerged (see Fig. 33).

Deformation   The tectonic conditions were generally quiet and original deformation is slight. Later movements in the Kaikoura Orogeny caused folding and faulting, in places severe, particularly on the east coast.

41

Figure 37 A magnificent display of stalactite and stalagmite development in a cave at Waitomo, in Oligocene limestone. *Photo: D.L. Homer*

Miocene M, *M*

Distribution Miocene rocks are well preserved throughout New Zealand, although previously they were even more extensive. The greatest extent of sedimentary rocks is in the west of the North Island, but there are large areas on the east coast too. Miocene sediments occur in mainly isolated patches right around the South Island, but are particularly extensive in the northwest and far south. Although volcanic rocks of Miocene age are found mainly in Northland and Coromandel, they also form the protrusions of Banks and Otago peninsulas and minor areas in eastern Otago in the South Island (Fig. 38).

Content The majority of Miocene sediments are marine in origin, particularly in the North Island. The most typical rock form is sequences of alternating sandstone and mudstone particularly in the north and west of the North Island. In Northland some areas

mapped as Miocene are composed of a chaotic assortment of blocks of older rocks; the Miocene age relates only to the age of emplacement of this chaos breccia. Pods of serpentine are commonly associated with the latter lithology. Further south, around Auckland and environs, the Miocene is typically represented by rather soft alternating mudstone and sandstone, with more massive beds of sandstone, and minor occurrences of conglomerate, grit, and limestone. There are large areas of Miocene rocks from south of the Waikato River to North Taranaki. These rocks are mainly alternating sandstone and mudstone sequences, massive mudstone, and rare limestone. Coal measures are rare. The Upper Miocene is characterised by the development of concretionary mudstone and more common conglomerate. Tuffaceous bands are common in the Upper Miocene, particularly in the northern districts. On the east coast of the North Island, Miocene rocks are preserved in isolated basins. In

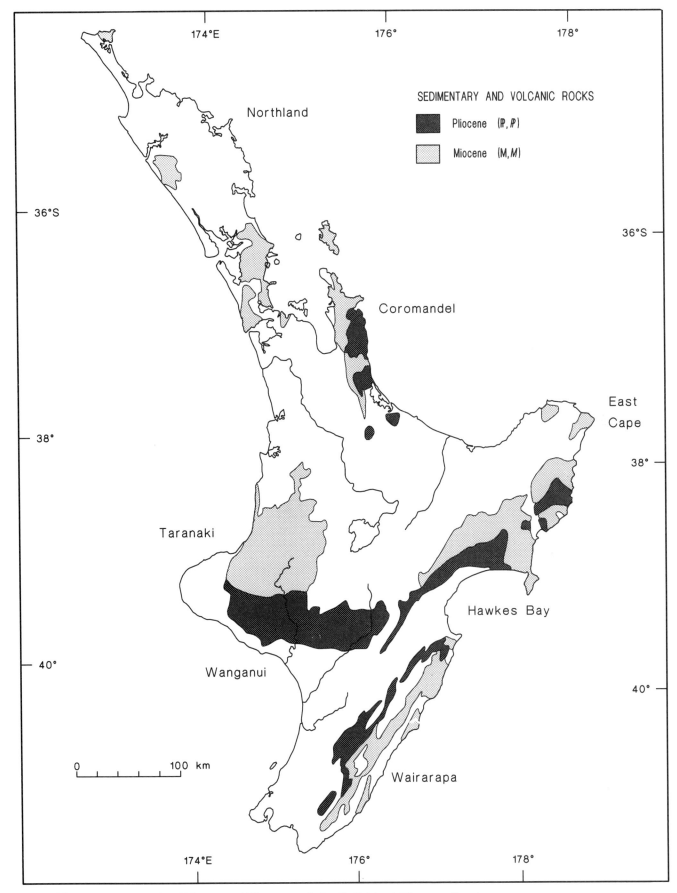

Figure 38 Distribution of rocks of Miocene and Pliocene age in the North Island. (Figure continued next page)

43

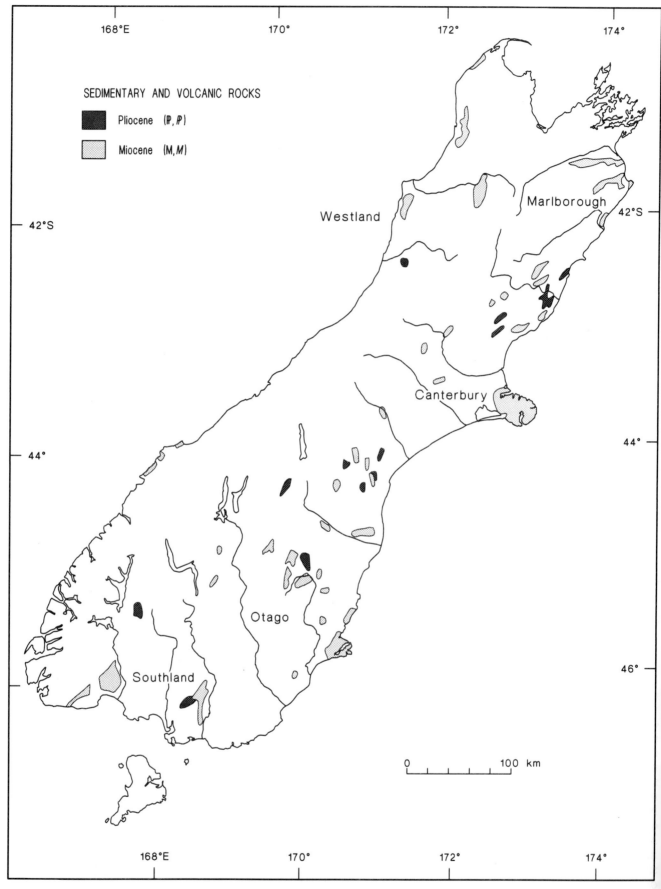

SEDIMENTARY AND VOLCANIC ROCKS

Pliocene (℗, ℙ)

Miocene (M, *M*)

Westland

Marlborough

Canterbury

Otago

Southland

0   100 km

Figure 38   (Continued)   Distribution of rocks of Miocene and Pliocene age in the South Island.

Figure 39 Alternating sequence of Miocene age sandstone and mudstone, stands almost vertical in this dramatic shore-platform exposure north of Castlepoint. Graded bedding and other sedimentary features indicate that the original base of this sequence is now towards the right.

Photo: D.L. Homer

general the Lower Miocene rocks are mudstone with minor sandstone and conglomerate, while alternating sequences (Fig. 39) are more commonly Middle Miocene in age. Upper Miocene rocks tend to be more tuffaceous and there are massive beds of blue-grey sandstone and mudstone (papa).

Miocene deposits in the northeast of the South Island are characterised by large amounts of marine conglomerate, particularly in the Wairau and Awatere valleys. Calcareous mudstone and sandstone are more common nearer the coast. In inland Canterbury non-marine deposits of sandstone, conglomerate, and mudstone are typical of the Late Miocene whereas marine mudstone and coarse sandstone are representative of earlier Miocene times, as well as being more common nearer the coast and further south into North Otago (Fig. 40). A phosphatic sandstone is the only marine sediment south of Dunedin, with all other Miocene deposits in the southeast being non-marine, including coal measures and oil shale. Marine deposition, however, continued in the Waiau River area of Southland, with a sequence of mudstone, limestone, micaceous sandstone, and coarse sandstone. The northwest of the South Island from Greymouth through to Nelson is an area of extensive Miocene deposition which is characterised by great thicknesses of brown or blue-grey mudstone and sandstone, locally

in alternating sequences. The youngest Miocene rocks here are non-marine conglomerate, sand, and coal measures. Further south near Jackson Bay, a small area of limestone, conglomerate, and alternating sandstone and mudstone is of Miocene age.

Volcanic activity was rampant in the Miocene. Andesite, basalt, and dacite with volcanic breccia in Northland, are but remnants of huge volcanoes that existed off the present west coast. The Waitakere Ranges, west of Auckland and the hills near Tokatoka, further north, are composed of andesite, volcanic breccia, and volcanic sediments, while basalt is present near Waipoua. Andesite, dacite, and rhyolite around Whangarei probably represent separate volcanic outlets. In the Coromandel area andesite and volcanic breccia are the most common Miocene rocks, although there are some areas of basaltic andesite as well as areas of rhyolite and dacite. Many of the offshore islands of Coromandel and Northland are of Miocene volcanic origin. Minor plutonic intrusions were associated with the volcanic activity, including the granite and diorite of Doubtless Bay, and diorite south of Cape Colville and that making up Cuvier Island. In the South Island, Miocene volcanoes spewed out mainly basalt lavas to build the Otago and Banks peninsulas. The two harbours of Banks Pensinula are both breached volcanic craters. The Otago Peninsula

45

Figure 40 Massive coarse sandstone of Miocene age forms this spectacular cliff south of Dunedin. Bedding is close to horizontal.   *Photo: D.L. Homer*

is made up of basalt with a high alkali content (Fig. 41), and the harbour here is the result of later downwarping. Inland from the Otago Peninsula areas of similar rocks occur, while Miocene basalt and tuff also occur in mid Canterbury.

Paleogeographic conditions At the end of the Oligocene the New Zealand area was just about under water. At the beginning of the Miocene, a new round of tectonic activity and mountain building started. This had the effect of uplifting the central part of the South Island, so that coastal areas were still experiencing marine conditions while the environment inland became progressively non-marine. The vast quantities of conglomerate in the Marlborough area reflect rapidly rising and eroding ground. The earth movements, however, were not simple uplift; there were varying degrees of uplift, downwarping, and buckling caused by the tectonic stresses. Thus in the west of the South Island a series of parallel basins developed which were continually downwarping and collecting vast quantities of sediment, especially around Murchison. In the Waiau River area in Southland another trough, which had developed at the end of the Eocene, continued to downwarp and collect sediment throughout the Miocene.

In the North Island the pattern was one of isolated basins continually developing, subsiding, and filling, a pattern which was particularly well developed

in the east coast area where the rocks can vary markedly in type and thickness within a few kilometres. There is no one place which has an unbroken record of the Miocene (an indication of the general mobility); terrestrial deposits interbedded with marine deposits confirm this. The sediments would all have been derived from the eroding centre of the North Island which was above sea level, and mainly deposited in fairly shallow water. In Northland, and probably the East Cape area too, the tectonic movements were sufficiently violent to disrupt the already deposited, mainly consolidated rocks of pre-Miocene age, in such a way as to transport them from their original depositional site and emplace large blocks in a chaotic manner in another site. An example of this tectonic disruption is shown in Fig. 42, which shows an oil well drilled at Waimamaku through an inverted sequence of Cretaceous and Eocene sediments. One theory of mechanism of emplacement invokes submarine gravity sliding.

Volcanic activity is generally associated with crustal movement and the Miocene is no exception. The effect of the volcanism was widespread, because many of the sediments have interbedded tuff layers.

Deformation The Miocene saw the start of a new phase of crustal activity and mountain building— the Kaikoura Orogeny. The movements continued throughout the Miocene and on through the Pliocene to the present day. The effects, however, varied from

46

Figure 41 Miocene basalt showing columnar jointing in a quarry in Dunedin. *Photo: D.L. Homer*

place to place. In some areas such as eastern Southland, gentle tilting took place, while elsewhere, as described above for Northland and East Cape, tremendous movement took place. In general, deformation was more severe in the east than the west so that local folding and faulting from Wairarapa to north of Gisborne is very marked. Soft-sediment deformation is also common as seen in slump folding within bedded units. In the west of the North Island beds are folded and faulted, but not so severely, and locally horizons can be followed for some distance. In the South Island the rapidly rising Southern Alps caused marked tilting, and debris flows are common, particularly in the northeastern area. On the western side the activity appears to have been more gentle, with broad open folds, although there are local areas of more intense deformation, particularly associated with fault movement.

Pliocene P, P

Distribution Pliocene sediments are most extensive in the south and east of the North Island. They also have a limited extent on both coasts of the South Island and in Southland. While Pliocene sediments are rare in the north of the North Island, volcanic rocks are present in both Northland and Coromandel (see Fig. 38).

Content Wanganui, Hawkes Bay, and Wairarapa areas were the major sites of Pliocene deposition. The sediments in the Wanganui area are chiefly mudstone and sandstone with common shellbeds and rare limestone and conglomerate bands, the latter being more common near the Ruahine Range. In Hawkes Bay and Wairarapa the Pliocene sediments are characterised by the presence of coquina limestone (loosely

47

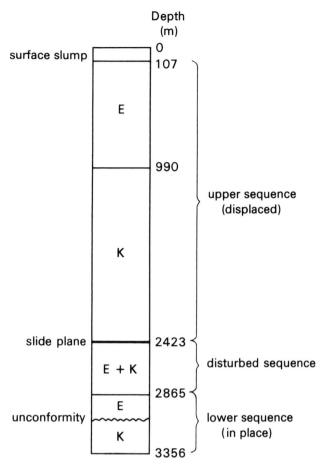

Depth (m)

surface slump — 0 / 107

E

990

upper sequence (displaced)

K

slide plane — 2423

E + K — disturbed sequence

2865

E

unconformity — lower sequence (in place)

K

3356

Figure 42 Diagrammatic well log of Waimamaku-2, an oil-prospecting well situated 10 km southeast of Hokianga Harbour mouth, Northland. The lowermost part (2865–3356 m) is an in-place sequence of Late Cretaceous to Late Eocene age. The uppermost Cretaceous to Eocene sequence (107–2423 m) has slid or been thrust over the lower, with a disturbed sequence of mixed Oligocene to Cretaceous rocks between.

cemented shelly deposit composed mainly of barnacle plates) which forms prominent scarp features. The coquina bands have a large lens-like form enclosed by thick muddy sandstone or sandy mudstone; there can be a transitional change from limestone into calcareous sandstone. Tuff bands are common throughout the Pliocene sequence. North of Gisborne, limestone becomes rare and calcareous sandstone more common. Minor marine deposits of sandstone with shellbeds followed by non-marine mudstone, are present on the coast south of Auckland, while non-marine mudstone and pumice breccia occur near Tauranga. In the South Island marine mudstone and concretionary sandy mudstone are present near Ward while in North Canterbury near Parnassus, mudstone with conglomerate, and minor limestone are present. Marine sandstone is also known from the Waiau River in Southland and muddy sandstone and calcareous mudstone are present near Greymouth and further south at Jackson Bay. Non-marine deposits of conglomerate and freshwater sand, with or without lignite layers are found throughout the South Island, in particular in Central Otago, Southland, inland Canterbury, northern Westland, and in Nelson.

Volcanism continued from the Miocene into the Pliocene in Northland and Coromandel, with andesite and volcanic breccia being present at Whangaroa

(Fig. 43), basalt at Ti Point, and widespread rhyolite, volcanic breccia, and minor andesite and dacite in eastern and southern parts of the Coromandel Peninsula (Fig. 44). The oldest parts of Pirongia and Karioi volcanoes on the west coast of the North Island are Pliocene in age as are the earliest ignimbrites in the Taupo Volcanic Zone. Some of the youngest eruptions of Banks Peninsula in the South Island may be Pliocene in age. Basalt eruptions in the Pliocene, together with tuffaceous sediments, built up the major parts of Auckland and Campbell islands far south of New Zealand as well as parts of the Chatham Islands.

Paleogeographic conditions The southern and eastern areas of the North Island were under water, and rapidly subsiding troughs were filled with sediment derived from rising land to the west and north. Generally, sedimentation kept pace with subsidence and the deposits were mainly in shallow water, with some exceptions. In the east, conditions favoured the growth of barnacle banks on the edges of deeper water channels.

The central part of the South Island was above sea level, while the eastern part of the Canterbury–Marlborough region was undergoing warping and faulting, allowing local invasion by the sea. The rising mountain areas contributed masses of detritus to freshwater lakes, and fans built up at the base of the rising blocks. Some areas of subsidence near Murchison and in the Moutere Depression accumulated vast quantities of gravel.

Deformation Movements of the Kaikoura Orogeny continued throughout the Pliocene, but most Pliocene rocks are not highly deformed and generally they have been gently folded or tilted. In some areas of active faulting the beds have been dragged up so that they are nearly vertical.

Quaternary ℚ ℚ, ℚ ℚ

Distribution There are no areas in New Zealand entirely free of Quaternary sediments, even if it is only present-day river alluvium or slope debris. Quaternary deposits are an important part of the present-day landscape and wide tracts of country are entirely of Quaternary origin, such as the sand dune deposits of Northland, the huge volcanic plateau of the central North Island, the alluvial plains of Hawkes Bay, Wairarapa, Canterbury, and Southland, and the glacial deposits of the west coast of the South Island.

Content In the North Island, sediments of both marine and non-marine origin occur, and volcanic deposits are widespread in the north. South Island sediments are all non-marine except for a small area in North Canterbury, and volcanic deposits are very limited.

Marine sediments are all of early Quaternary age and are restricted to the Wanganui, Wairarapa, Hawkes Bay (Fig. 45), and Bay of Plenty areas, and around Parnassus in southern Marlborough. In general these are shallow water deposits of sand and mud with shellbeds and some limestone, commonly with a high

Figure 43 Taratara, near Whangaroa in Northland is composed of andesitic breccia of Pliocene
age.   *N.Z.G.S. photo*

Figure 44 The Pinnacles, in the Coromandel Range east of Thames, consist of the eroded cores of
rhyolite domes erupted during Pliocene times.   *Photo: D.L. Homer*

Figure 45 Sandstone and mudstone of early Quaternary age lie in low dipping beds composing dissected hill country east of Lake Tutira. Hawke Bay in background. *Photo: D.L. Homer*

pumice and ash content particularly in the Bay of Plenty and northern areas of Hawkes Bay. Barnacle coquina limestone is present in the Wairarapa, whereas the limestone in Hawkes Bay is made up of other shelly material (Fig. 46) and contains more muddy lenses.

Non-marine deposits vary depending on their locality, with glacial deposits being predominant in the South Island, and fluvial and aeolian sediments common in the North Island. In the north of the North Island, lake muds, fluviatile gravel and sand with a high pumice and ash content, and commonly forming terraces, represent the early Quaternary. Dune sands started to build the Ninety Mile Beach and the prominent bars to the Kaipara, Manukau, Raglan, Kawhia, and Tauranga harbours. In the southern part of the North Island gravel derived from the rapidly rising mountain ranges was deposited at the margins of the marine basins. Later in the Quaternary the marine basins had disappeared and the deposits were mainly fluviatile gravels and sands. Spectacular flights of river and coastal terraces were formed at this time, as well as the bulk of dune deposits around the coasts, the dunes of the Manawatu plains (see Fig. 10) being a

fine example. A loose very fine grained wind-blown deposit called loess is widespread and quite thick in some parts of the south of the North Island.

In the South Island, lower Quaternary deposits are thick fluviatile gravels with sandy or muddy lenses; the gravels are particularly extensive in the Moutere Depression near Nelson and further west, but also occur in Central Otago and Southland. The oldest gravels in these areas are probably Pliocene in age but deposition continued well into the Quaternary. Later on in the Quaternary the deposits are mainly glacial in origin, with till and outwash gravels being particularly prominent on the West Coast and in the mountainous areas (Fig. 47). The Canterbury Plains are built up from outwash gravel, and once extended beyond the present-day coastline. The thick loess deposits on the terrace surfaces and on other rock surfaces in Canterbury and further south also date from this time. In many areas around the coast there are remnants of marine benches, as well as substantial dune accumulation, while inland, valleys were infilled with alluvium and river terraces subsequently formed.

The products of intense Quaternary volcanism are readily visible in the northern part of the North Island.

50

Figure 46   Coquina limestone of early Quaternary age at Castlepoint. The rock is entirely composed
of shell material, the predominant type being bivalve molluscs.   *Photo: D.L. Homer*

Figure 47   Ridges (lateral moraines) beside Lake Pukaki in the Mackenzie country were formed
from debris carried on the sides of a glacier which flowed down the valley during the last glaciation.
                                                                    Photo: D.L. Homer

51

Figure 48   Mount Tarawera, in the Bay of Plenty, consists of several rhyolite domes. The rift in the centre was formed in 1886 by the last eruption, when basaltic ash was erupted and a dike intruded. Mount Edgecumbe is visible at extreme top left (see Fig. 7).   *Photo: D.L. Homer*

The main area of volcanic rock is concentrated in a "V" shaped area with the Tongariro National Park volcanoes forming the southern apex and widening to include the Rotorua area and most of the Bay of Plenty. This area is known as the Taupo Volcanic Zone. The most common rock type in the zone is ignimbrite, formed when extremely explosive eruptions forced vast glowing clouds of hot gaseous ash and debris to flow at great speed to considerable distances from their source— up to 60 kilometres. The heat in the flow caused the particles to weld together. The ignimbrite forms flat topped plateau areas (see Fig. 6) which are common around and north of Lake Taupo and can be up to 150 metres thick. Other types of eruptions formed rhyolite domes such as those around Rotorua and Taupo, notably Mounts Tarawera (Fig. 48), Ngongotaha, and Tauhara, and dacite is present south of Rotorua. Eruptions were not only of lava, but copious quantities of ash and pumice were also erupted to settle in great thicknesses over the landscape. Ash and pumice are major constituents of Quaternary sediments in areas quite a distance from the volcanic activity. Pumice, particularly, is found a

long way from its origin, (e.g., on Wellington beaches), as it is light enough to float and is easily transported by the sea and rivers. The more recent eruptions of the Taupo Volcanic Zone have been andesitic in character, as demonstrated by the Tongariro Park volcanoes, Mount Edgecumbe, and White Island, while the most recent eruption of Mount Tarawera in 1886 was basaltic (see Fig. 48).

Quaternary volcanism was not confined to the Taupo Volcanic Zone. In Northland and around Auckland city, basaltic volcanoes were active, erupting basalt and building scoria cones. Offshore, Little Barrier Island was formed from andesite, and islands east of Coromandel from andesitic and rhyolitic eruptions. Basalt and basaltic andesite were erupted in the Kermadec Islands. On the west coast, Pirongia and Karioi built up cones of basaltic andesite in the early Quaternary, while at the same time in the Taranaki region the Sugar Loaf Islands were built of andesite. The Taranaki volcanism then migrated south through the cones of Kaitake and Pouakai to Egmont, all andesitic in character and successively younger in age.

A particular type of deposit associated with the

Figure 49 Lahar mounds to the west of Mount Egmont, Taranaki, formed by an avalanche of volcanic debris from Egmont.

Photo: D.L. Homer

volcanic centres of Tongariro and Taranaki is that formed by lahars. This deposit is made up of a chaotic assortment of volcanic material which has flowed down the mountain and then spread out over the surrounding countryside. A lahar may be generated by collapse of a volcanic cone, by earthquake activity, or by particularly heavy rainfall. If water from a crater lake is involved, the amount and size of debris that is transported and the distance travelled can be very large. During glacial periods the mountain tops were capped with ice and snow which melted when an eruption took place and was a source of water for transport. The type of countryside formed by lahars is very characteristic and well exemplified on the western slopes of Mount Egmont as a chaotic jumble of conical hills (Fig. 49).

In the South Island volcanism was not so extensive, but there is a considerable area of basalt dating from the early Quaternary inland and north of Timaru. Andesite forming Solander Island west of Foveaux Strait, and basalt forming the Antipodes Islands date from early Quaternary time.

It is relevant to consider present-day deposits, as we still exist in Quaternary time and geological processes are continuing. The material in present-day river valleys and beaches has been mainly deposited since the last glacial stage ended, about 14 000 years ago. From then until about 6000 years ago there was a substantial warming of climate which caused a rise in sea level; some cliffs, terraces, and dune deposits are recognised as having formed at the time the sea level rise ended. Sea level has dropped again slightly since that time. Lakes, including manmade ones, are presently collecting mud and sand and will eventually fill, while many river flood plains are building up with each flood. Sand dunes naturally advance, blown by the wind until stabilised by vegetation; evidence of Maori middens being covered by advancing dunes is common. Volcanoes may erupt to build higher cones or explode destructively; ash showers continue to fall on the land while geysers and boiling mud pools are evidence of activity beneath the ground. Earthquakes create deposits by shaking which causes landslides and further erosion.

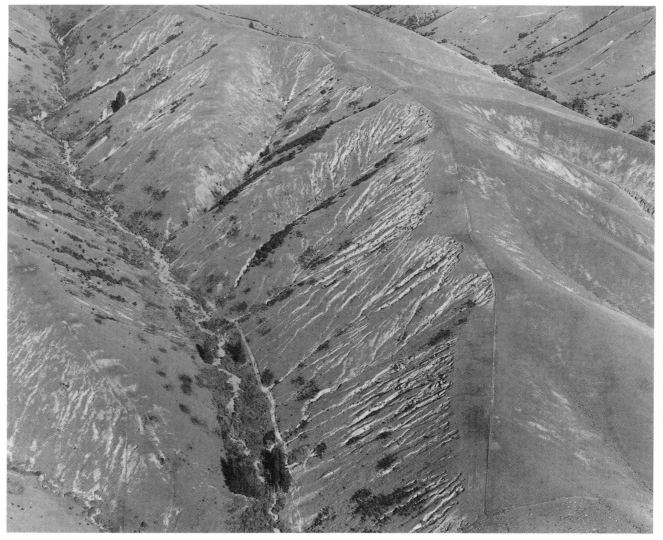

Figure 50 Gully erosion on cleared slopes in Marlborough.

Photo: D.L. Homer

Man is having a small effect on geological processes, mainly by controlling rivers, and developing the countryside. Floods are prevented by building stopbanks, channelling material out to sea instead of over the flood plain; this affects the build up of deltas and beaches, and erosion. River valleys can become choked with debris because clearance of natural vegetation and overstocking can cause landslides and gully erosion (Fig. 50), providing more material than the river can cope with. Coastal build-up and erosion is also affected by man's activities; building groynes and sea walls may protect one area but expose an adjacent area, while dredging sand and gravel can also affect the natural processes. Hydro-electric power schemes divert rivers and form lakes, markedly changing the natural fluviatile regime.

Paleogeographic conditions In the early Quaternary the southern part of the North Island was under a shallow sea, as were parts of the east and west coast of the South Island. By the mid Quaternary, earth movements, uplift, and deposition had brought New Zealand to roughly the shape it is today. The rapidly

rising areas of the Southern Alps contributed masses of debris to the rivers, and filled depressions and river valleys. Although it is possible that glaciations occurred during the early Quaternary it is not until about 500 000 years ago that there is firm evidence of widespread glaciation. During glacial periods the high parts of the Southern Alps were under a permanent ice field, and valley glaciers carved their way both west and east, and coalesced into ice sheets where the topography became more gentle. Vast amounts of debris were carried within and on top of the glaciers as well as pushed in front of them. This debris (till) was dumped when the ice melted and forms a distinctive hummocky ground surface, well illustrated by the topography of the Mackenzie basin (see Fig. 47). Meltwater from the glaciers carried debris away and formed large outwash fans. There were four major phases of glaciation, and each one had minor fluctuations. Each of these built up its own outwash plains, and successive terraces were subsequently cut by rivers draining through them. The spectacular terraces on the Canterbury Plains were built up in this way (see Fig. 8). The worldwide glaciations caused sea level to

54

drop, as much water was bound up in ice and snow. During warmer interglacial periods, the ice melted and sea level rose. The effect of these oscillating sea levels is clearly seen in coastal terraces, each flat surface marking the position of an earlier high sea level. Periods of low sea level and cold climate created expanses of bare earth and sand with little vegetation. Winds blew the coastal sand into dunes while dust particles were blown and deposited on rocky and planar surfaces to become loess.

In the North Island there was little active glaciation except in the very highest mountain areas. The effects of cold and oscillating sea levels were the same as for the South Island, so that marine benches and flights of river terraces were formed. The build up of sand dunes and loess accumulation, were a result of low sea levels and cold climate.

Deformation The Kaikoura Orogeny continued from the Pliocene throughout the Quaternary, as it does to the present-day, with earthquakes and fault movements. The New Zealand landscape, as we know it, is the result of this orogeny, as is the recent past and present volcanic activity. Some of the marine sediments of early Quaternary age are folded and tilted quite substantially especially if associated with faulting, but most sediments of Quaternary age are essentially flat-lying. Volcanism is certainly not extinct, as illustrated by continued activity in the Taupo Volcanic Zone.

History of deformation

Sedimentary rocks originally laid down in horizontal or gently sloping layers are rarely so today. They are more commonly steeply sloping (see Fig. 39) and may be warped, twisted, and broken (Fig. 51), so much so that in some places it is hard to see the original layering. Analysis of this deformation gives a clue to events in the past. Old rocks may have undergone many phases of deformation and each phase will have left its imprint. Younger rocks are generally less deformed. In some parts of the world very old rocks may lie in horizontal layers representing a long stable history, but in New Zealand this is not the case and even the very youngest rocks may be deformed.

Rock may be deformed either when it is hard and brittle, or while sediments are still soft or in a semi-solid state. Sediments or rocks are subject to stresses from movements within the earth's crust; these stresses may be compressional in which case the rock will buckle, fold, and may finally break, or they may be tensional which causes the rocks to stretch and break.

Figure 51   Severe folding and deformation of "greywacke" strata in Wellington, near a major fault.
Photo: D.L. Homer

Figure 52 Upper Triassic sandstone and mudstone (right) dipping eastward (to the left) at 60–70°, overlain by Eocene sandstone and mudstone forming sharp ridges dipping eastward at 30–40°. An unconformity separates the Triassic and Eocene rocks. The Eocene rocks have been folded by the Kaikoura Orogeny; the Triassic rocks have been affected by both the Rangitata and Kaikoura orogenies. View southwards along the eastern flank of Takitimu Mountains, Southland.

Photo: D.L. Homer

Figure 53 Part of the active Clarence Fault in Marlborough. Two parallel traces can be clearly seen, and note the clockwise (dextral) offset of the streams, on the lower trace to the left.

Photo: D.L. Homer

Once the rock has broken, further stress will be taken up along the fracture and the rocks on either side will move relative to each other, either in a vertical or horizontal sense, or sometimes both— a process known as faulting. Folding and faulting leads to a final rock outcrop pattern quite different from the original depositional one.

The stresses within the earth's crust during mountain building episodes are tremendous and the accompanying deformation of the rocks is usually severe. Areas a little removed from the main centre of deformation, however, may only suffer gentle tilting, or simple up and down movement along faults.

The first recognised phase of major mountain building occurred during the Silurian and Devonian and is known as the Tuhua Orogeny. The older rocks in Northwest Nelson and Fiordland underwent severe deformation during this orogeny; folding and faulting were intense, so much so that folded loops of sediment were dislocated from their base and pushed into a distant position (see Fig. 19). Heating from the intrusion of igneous rocks and pressure generated by compressive forces caused most sediments to become

slightly metamorphosed in Northwest Nelson and more so in Fiordland, although in the latter locality some rocks had been metamorphosed previously.

The next major episode of mountain building during Jurassic–Cretaceous time (Rangitata Orogeny) further deformed the older rocks, while severely contorting the rocks and sediments of the New Zealand Geosyncline. The intensity of the orogeny varied from place to place and the rocks most deformed were those in the central and deepest parts of the geosyncline. In the more marginal areas such as Kawhia and Southland the sediments were only gently folded. An example is the parallel anticlines and synclines that are clearly seen in Southland.

The third and continuing mountain building phase, which started in the Miocene, is the Kaikoura Orogeny. These movements have built up the mountain ranges that New Zealand is famous for today. In general, Tertiary rocks are gently folded and much less deformed than the older rocks; however, on the east coast of the North Island, in coastal Marlborough, and on the west of the South Island, they are quite severely folded, especially where they are near faults. Older

Tertiary rocks are more deformed than younger rocks, and there is generally an angular break (unconformity) between Tertiary and Mesozoic rocks (Fig. 52).

Lines of weakness (such as faults) created during one orogeny are liable to move again in subsequent orogenies. The major faults active during the Rangitata Orogeny became active again in the Kaikoura Orogeny, although the movement was not always in the same direction.

A feature of the Kaikoura Orogeny is transcurrent faulting, in which rocks are displaced (mainly horizontally) along a fault, often for great distances. The major transcurrent faults in the South Island and east coast of the North Island are shown on the map although many others exist, particularly in the Hawkes Bay–Wairarapa area. The Alpine Fault is the best indicator of movement, where there has been a 500 km displacement, estimated by matching up rock types in Nelson with similar types north of Milford Sound on the opposite side of the fault. It is a matter of continuing debate whether most of the movement took place in the Rangitata or Kaikoura orogeny. Faults demonstrating transcurrent movement in late Quaternary time are most obvious in the Marlborough region where there is good evidence of offset streams and terraces (Fig. 53).

In the North Island transcurrent faulting is evident throughout the East Coast area, the faulting being generally parallel to the coast and controlling the outcrop areas of the "greywacke" ranges. In the central areas of the North Island there is a different structural pattern, which shows the whole of the Taupo Volcanic Zone as being a down-dropped area in relation to the rest of the North Island. This may reflect collapse after ejection of magma, general contraction of the area as magma sank to a lower level, or be associated with subduction of the Pacific plate. Numerous faults trending parallel to the zone are present, the movement tending to be vertical rather than horizontal (see Fig. 57).

Some areas of New Zealand seem to have been little affected by the Kaikoura Orogeny. Northland for instance has been relatively stable since the Late Miocene, and experiences few earthquakes today. The Dunedin and Otago areas also experience relatively little earthquake activity.

Active faulting is the more obvious feature of present-day deformation, but in some areas of the North Island folding is occurring away from active fault movement. Recent tilting of the ground surface has been measured in the Manawatu plains, southeast Wairarapa and near Gisborne. All the present-day activity is related to the fact that the margin between the Indian–Australian and Pacific plates passes to the east of the North Island and through the South Island in the guise of the Alpine Fault.

Economic and applied geology

So far we have considered "geology" from a strictly academic viewpoint: Which rock is where? How old is it? How did it get there? In this section we look at the uses of geology, and the problems geology may create for present-day society. The uses may be considered in terms of the mineral resources within the rocks, while the problems arise from the development of those resources, or from the settlement and use of the land.

Mineral resources

"Mineral resources" covers a wide range of economically useful materials from the glamour of precious metals to that everyday essential, water. New Zealand's minerals are varied, but there are few particularly large or rich deposits. Nevertheless, because of material needs the search for new resources and the re-evaluation of known deposits is a continuing process. New technology may require different resources, while new methods and changing economic circumstances may allow the development of previously abandoned deposits.

Metallic minerals

Metals may occur in native (pure) form or combined with other elements as minerals, particularly as sulphides. If the metal can be extracted at a profit the mineral aggregate is called an ore. New Zealand is not particularly rich in metallic minerals, and many potentially metal-bearing rocks are in remote, rugged country, still not fully prospected (e.g., Fiordland). Native metals are usually found in association with quartz veins in old, igneous, or metamorphic rocks or in detrital form in terrace, river, or beach sands and gravels.

Gold and **silver** tend to occur together in native form and have been mined from quartz lodes in Coromandel, Northwest Nelson, and Central Otago, the Coromandel lodes proving very rich. Rich deposits of gold were also found in river terrace gravels and beach sands in the South Island, and were the basis of the "gold rush" in the late 1860s. These gold-bearing gravels were deposited by ancient rivers which eroded the gold from lodes and transported the grains downstream. The extensive dredge tailings resulting from gold mining are still evident on many river banks in Central Otago and the west coast of the South Island. Higher prices for gold in recent years have stimulated interest in both alluvial and lode gold mining, particularly in the South Island and Coromandel.

Copper has been mined as sulphide ore in Northland, southern Coromandel, and Northwest Nelson, and has also been found in association with granite intrusions, serpentinite, and high grade metamorphic rocks.

Lead and **zinc** in association with **gold** and **silver** have been mined from volcanic rocks in southern Coromandel. Other deposits of lead and zinc are known,

but not in economic quantities. Minor deposits of **antimony, chromium, manganese, mercury,** and **platinum** have been exploited at various times from Coromandel, Nelson, Northland, and Southland.

Uranium has been investigated in breccias near the Buller River, while **tungsten** ore is being mined from scheelite veins in schist at the head of Lake Wakatipu, at Macraes Flat (northern Otago), and near Blenheim. **Nickel, tin,** and **molybdenum** have been investigated but have not been found in economic quantities.

Iron ore was mined at Onekaka from Paleozoic rocks in Northwest Nelson, but by far the greatest resources are in beach and dune sands of Quaternary age along the west coast of the North Island. Here the iron occurs in the form of titanomagnetite, a mineral derived from volcanic rocks. The ironsand is used to make steel near Auckland, and is also magnetically concentrated and shipped overseas from Waipipi and Taharoa. Ilmenite sands near Westport have potential as a source of **titanium,** a major component of the mineral ilmenite.

Construction materials

One of the major needs in New Zealand is **aggregate** for the construction of roads, as a building material, and to make concrete. Aggregate consists of small fragments of hard rock, and can either be taken direct from naturally occurring river or beach gravels, or derived by crushing solid rock. The main requirements are that the rock be hard, unweathered, and not contain minerals that may cause the rock to disintegrate later, as a result of pressure or chemical reactions. Suitable rocks for aggregate are some volcanic rocks, hard sandstone and limestone, plutonic rocks and some metamorphic rocks. Although many areas of New Zealand are well off for aggregate, there are problems in obtaining good quality aggregate in areas of soft Tertiary rocks, or very weathered rock. Protection against over-exploitation of aggregate for environmental reasons is desirable in some areas; for instance too much gravel taken from a river bed can alter its course, cause scouring of banks and structures, and may affect groundwater quality. Town Planning regulations may be necessary to preserve valuable aggregate resources from urban development.

Building stone is often imported into New Zealand, although a number of local rock types are suitable. However, some are in remote areas, and transport costs, plus high labour costs in processing the stone, make the use of many New Zealand building stones uneconomic in a limited market. A well known building stone is Ordovician marble from Takaka Hill, near Nelson, and schist from Central Otago makes an attractive ornamental stone, particularly for fireplaces. Igneous rocks such as granite make good building stone, while ignimbrite from the North Island is easily worked and is common as a facing material on houses. Tertiary age Oamaru Limestone has been widely used for public buildings and, although the stone on some buildings has suffered badly from corrosion over the years, it is still quarried.

Sand is used for construction, in making concrete and in plastering; suitable deposits are widespread in beaches, dunes, and river beds.

Manufacturing materials

A commonly required material for all sorts of manufacturing is **clay**, and many different types of clay are available for different uses. The ceramic industry uses kaolin and halloysite from Northland for china and earthenware, while other clays are more suitable for brick and tile manufacture. Clay occurs as a weathering product of many different rock types, or as an original deposit, and is widespread throughout the country although large quantities of high quality clay are not common. A naturally swelling variety of clay called **bentonite** is found on the east coast of the North Island and a non-swelling variety in North Canterbury can be treated chemically to make it swell. Both are used as a drilling mud as well as for other industrial purposes.

Diatomite is a siliceous deposit of minute organisms. It is used as a filter or insulator, and is found in a marine Tertiary deposit in Oamaru, as well as in some freshwater Quaternary deposits in the North Island.

Pumice is a considerable resource in the centre of the North Island, and is used as an abrasive or insulator.

Sand has many uses in manufacturing, particularly for moulding in foundry work and as an abrasive. A particularly pure quartz variety (**silica sand**) is used in glass manufacture. This type of sand is dredged from Quaternary sands on the sea floor off Kokota Spit in Northland, is dug from coastal terraces of Quaternary age near Glorit (north of Helensville), and is quarried from a lowermost Tertiary sequence at Mount Somers in Canterbury.

Limestone with a suitable content of calcium carbonate is used for cement manufacture, and in the manufacture of steel, paper, and glass. The main resources are of Oligocene age at Whangarei, Te Kuiti, Takaka, and Dunedin, but other deposits of varying quality and age occur throughout the country.

Greenstone (New Zealand jade) is an attractive mineral found in parts of Westland. It is used in the manufacture of ornaments and jewellery.

Agricultural materials (fertilisers)

The main use of **limestone** is for agricultural lime, as New Zealand soils tend to be rather acid. There are many limestone deposits throughout the country suitable for this purpose. **Dolomite** contains magnesium carbonate and is used to enrich soils with a low magnesium content (it is also used in glass manufacture). It is found in an Ordovician marble near Collingwood in the north of the South Island. The application of superphosphate is facilitated by the addition of **serpentine**. Isolated bodies of serpentinite are found in Northland and southern Waikato, and bands of the material are present in Permian sequences in Nelson and northwestern Otago.

Phosphate has been quarried from Tertiary sediments south of Dunedin, and other minor occurrences have been noted in association with glauconitic sandstone. Investigations are being pursued into the feasibility of mining nodular phosphorite from the sea floor on the Chatham Rise. **Sulphur** associated with volcanic activity is found in the Taupo–Rotorua area, where there is a large, but low grade deposit at Lake Rotokawa. Sulphur was mined from White Island until a volcanic eruption in 1914 made the exercise too dangerous.

Mineral fuels

At the present time there is considerable concern about energy resources, and the rising costs of imported fuels. The search for **oil** and **gas** has been continuing since the late 1800s with little success until recently. Prospects looked good in the early days as there were numerous reports of oil seeps and gas blows, but most investigations came to nothing. The only commercial field was in New Plymouth where a few barrels of oil per day were produced from 1934 to 1972. A big breakthrough was made in the early 1960s when the Kapuni gas field was discovered, and a few years later the large Maui field was found offshore. Both these gas fields are contained within a non-marine coal measure unit of Eocene age. Some of the oil wells that have been drilled offshore have been illustrated on the map, and indicate the rock sequences they encountered. In 1980 drilling north of Stratford proved a small oilfield (McKee) with commercial potential, and prospective structures nearby are at present being drilled. Attractive prospects remain to be investigated, particularly in offshore basins. Thus drilling has continued in the Tasman Sea, Hawke Bay, and the Great South Basin, south and east of Stewart Island and Otago. The target horizons, those thought most likely to be oil bearing, are beds generally of Late Cretaceous–early Tertiary age. **Oil shale** is a hard mudstone which when crushed and heated in a retort releases oil; deposits have been investigated in Otago and Southland.

Investigation of **coal** resources in New Zealand has been important from the early days of colonisation. Bituminous coal is produced only from the West Coast coalfields of Greymouth, Buller, and Reefton, which are of Late Cretaceous to Eocene age. Generally the rank, sulphur, and ash content of the coals vary considerably in these West Coast coalfields, and the coals are suited to a variety of uses. Large deposits of sub-bituminous coal are present in the North Island, particularly the Waikato area, where the Huntly, Maramarua, Rotowaro, and Glen Massey fields have been the main producers. Ohai and Kaitangata have been major coal producing areas from Cretaceous sub-bituminous deposits in the South Island. There are numerous minor coal occurrences of varying ages throughout the country. A renewed interest in coal in recent years has led to the discovery of very large lignite reserves in Southland and Central Otago, and to proving large sub-bituminous coal reserves from Hamilton to North Taranaki. However, in both areas there could be considerable problems in the development of mines. It is envisaged that these coals, if they can be mined economically, will, among other projects, be used to provide electric power and be processed to liquid fuels.

61

Groundwater

This is a major and increasingly important resource, even in a high-rainfall country like New Zealand. Many endeavours, be they manufacturing, agricultural, or social, depend on the availability of water for their success. Water is a necessity of life, and when rainwater or surface water is not sufficient, groundwater can be utilised. For instance, the water supply of 13 large urban areas, including Christchurch, Napier, Hastings, and Palmerston North, is entirely from groundwater reserves.

Water is present in all rocks below a certain level (the water table), and is constantly replenished by rain and surface water percolating through the ground. A rock layer carrying water is called an aquifer. When a well is drilled into an aquifer the water is usually pumped to the ground surface, but sometimes water (confined under pressure) will rise to the surface without being pumped and is then called artesian.

The best-known and largest groundwater systems are those underlying alluvial plains in Hawkes Bay, Wairarapa, Wairau, Waimea, and Canterbury. The aquifers are gravel or coarse sand layers of Quaternary age, that are recharged from rivers flowing across the plains, that themselves receive water from the rain in the mountains. These groundwater systems support thriving farming and horticultural industries. The water within the groundwater system has collected over thousands of years, but can become depleted if drawoff exceeds recharge. Without due care, contamination by sea water intrusion near the coast, sewage, fertiliser, or industrial spillage may occur.

A special type of groundwater provides electricity and heating— **geothermal steam**. In areas of recent volcanic activity where the ground is still hot, groundwater temperatures may exceed boiling point. When wells are drilled into the water-bearing strata, the superheated water is discharged under great pressure. The system is recharged by rain and surface water percolating through the hot rocks. A steam field at Wairakei is exploited for electricity generation, other fields nearby and in Northland have the potential for development. Geothermal steam is used directly by industry at Kawerau, while many factories and homes use hot water for central heating in Rotorua and Taupo. Hot water springs and pools occur in many places throughout the country usually associated either with recent volcanic activity, or with active faulting. Over-use can deplete geothermal fields, and may cause ground subsidence.

Geological problems

Geological factors can have a profound influence on any major land-use or development project. The suitability of foundation conditions for an industrial site, the likelihood of landslides disrupting road or rail linkages, the stability of slopes in a hillside housing complex, and the effects of earthquake shaking, faulting, or volcanic eruption, are all geological considerations that should be evaluated when decisions are made to develop the land. The geological problems most likely to be met can be conveniently dealt with under two main headings: land stability and geological hazards, even though there is some overlap.

Land stability

New Zealand is a geologically young country with an actively developing topography. The continuing uplift and accompanying severe erosion has led to the formation of steep slopes, many of them potentially unstable. Causes of instability are many and varied, but mainly depend on the rock composition, the attitude of the rocks relative to the slope, fractures, and the amount of water present. In some areas rocks have been exposed to the weather for many thousands of years, and the weathering process has produced a mantle of weak material many metres thick on top of the solid unweathered rock. The weathered mantle is very prone to slumping, as is debris (such as slopewash) which collects over many years on hill slopes. Water is usually a very important factor in land stability. It is no coincidence that many slips occur after heavy rain or prolonged wet periods. The water reduces friction in the sliding process, while also making the material heavier and more likely to succumb to gravitational forces.

Man often interferes with the natural processes. Slopes that were stable at one angle, may not be at a steeper one; removing vegetation and the natural debris cover allows greater infiltration of water and exposes rock to accelerated weathering which may cause failure several years later. Changing the surface water run-off pattern can cause scouring.

Natural erosion of river banks and coastal cliffs is a common cause of landslipping, and undercutting is particularly severe during storms when the sea or river is carrying more debris and is therefore more abrasive. Development along cliffs (Fig. 54) has to be investigated very carefully as coastal erosion may only be alleviated by the expensive construction of a sea wall which often has only a temporary effect.

Developments involving steep slopes need careful engineering to minimise the risk of failure. Planning the routes of roads, railways, and pipelines should take the local geology into account; it may be better to take a longer route and avoid unstable country. Where there is no choice, the cut slopes must be designed with the least likelihood of failure and, if necessary, extensive support systems installed.

Siting of hydro-electric dams has to take into account the strength of the rock because the abutments have to bear the weight of the structure. The conditions of the slopes around a hydro-lake must also be considered, because extensive wetting of the lower part of a slope may cause failure. Foundation conditions for industrial complexes and large structures are important as some materials decrease in volume when loaded, causing buildings to settle and crack.

Land stability also plays an important role in agriculture. Wholesale clearing of forests has caused increased run-off and infiltration of rainwater and in many areas landsliding has resulted. Grazing of large numbers of stock on steep slopes may cause superficial failures (see Fig. 50); the effect is to remove pasture, and as grass does not readily grow back onto bare rock, the amount of production is decreased. Landsliding in the heads of river valleys can lead to choking of river systems further down the valley and more loss of productive land.

Figure 54   The dangers of developing too close to an eroding coastline are readily apparent from this photograph taken near Tauranga.   *Photo: D.L. Homer*

Geological hazards

The hazards considered here are those from naturally occurring phenomena that are not consequent on the activities of man. In the previous section land instability was reviewed in terms of normally occurring natural and manmade causes; however, it must be pointed out that major landslides can also be caused by both earthquake and volcanic activity.

There are two types of **earthquake hazard**: (a) ground shaking which can have a wide-ranging effect and cause failure of structures, distortion of roads (Fig. 55) and railways, and landsliding, up to a considerable distance from the earthquake epicentre; (b) ground rupture which is a local effect causing damage to structures and ground close to the rupture.

Earthquakes are generated by movement within the earth's crust and upper mantle ranging from a few tens of metres to hundreds of kilometres below the surface. Shock waves travel through the rock strata and release energy at the surface, causing different materials to respond in different ways. In general, hard consolidated rock shakes less than soft, loose material. Thus movement is felt more intensely on alluvial plains than on surrounding hill country formed of solid

rock. The hazardous effects of shaking vary in distance and intensity from the epicentre depending on the magnitude and depth of the earthquake and the geological structure of the area. In New Zealand, building codes are enforced so that structures can withstand shaking from all but the most severe earthquakes.

Some large shallow earthquakes may cause the ground surface to rupture and crack, usually along well defined lines (faults) where movement has occurred before. Structures built across these faults will be destroyed in the case of rupture, so it is important to be able to identify them.

Geological mapping can identify faults by recognising reference features that were once joined, such as stream courses (see Fig. 53) or terraces; knowing the age of the reference feature helps assess when the last movement took place and how often movement occurs. Any movement within the last 500 000 years classifies a fault as "active". It is recommended that no structures should be built within 20 metres of an active fault. Areas most subject to faulting and earthquake activity are shown on Fig. 56, but no area in New Zealand can be considered free of the risk of earthquake activity.

Figure 55   Damage to a road near Inangahua, after the earthquake there in 1968.

Photo: D.L. Homer

At present the area most obviously susceptible to **volcanic hazard** is the Taupo Volcanic Zone (Fig. 57), where there have been continuing eruptions in historic time. Most eruptions over the last 100 years have been minor events erupting mainly ash and little lava. From the geologic record it is obvious that past eruptions have been very violent indeed and such events can be expected again. The explosive eruption of Tarawera in 1886, which caused widespread devastation and the loss of 150 lives, is indicative of the type of eruption that could happen. It is quite possible that even larger eruptions could occur. The emptying of the crater lake at Mount Ruapehu is certain to occur reasonably frequently, though there is now a warning device in use which should prevent another disaster like Tangiwai in 1953. Although the immediate hazard is close to the volcano, volcanic ash can have an

effect a considerable distance from the source by killing off vegetation and polluting water supplies.

Other areas considered potentially hazardous are Taranaki and Auckland. Although these areas have not experienced an eruption for some time, they are certainly not considered extinct. The last eruption at Mount Egmont was 200 years ago as dated by an ash shower burying Maori ovens, while Rangitoto certainly erupted about 600 years ago and may have erupted since. These may seem long intervals to man, but geologically they are very short indeed.

Tsunamis are unusually high sea waves generated by movement of the sea floor caused by earthquakes or volcanic activity. They can create havoc as they may devastate low-lying areas, which happened in Indonesia after the Krakatoa eruption in 1883. Several

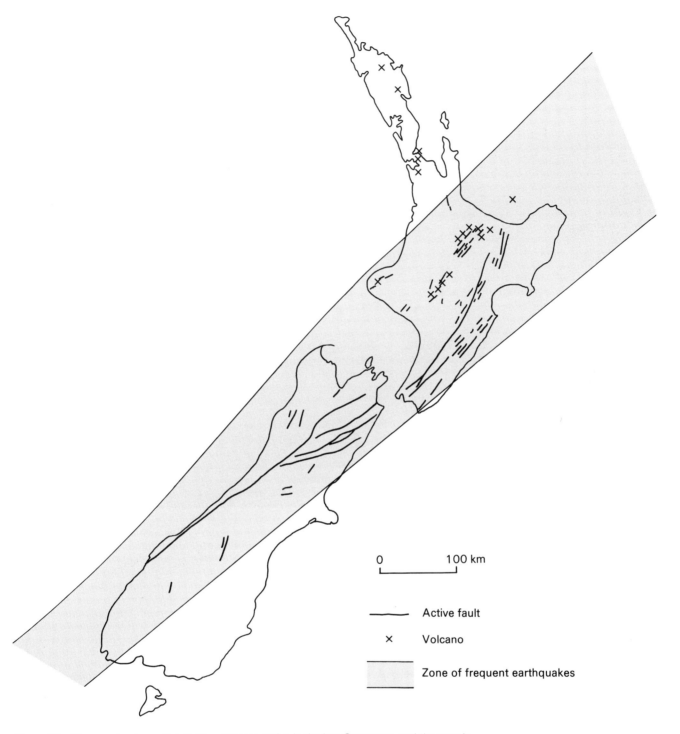

Figure 56 Diagram showing active faults, volcanoes active in the late Quaternary, and the zone in which earthquakes occur most frequently.

Figure 57 The volcanic plateau of Tongariro National Park. The 3 active volcanoes from north to south (left to right) are Tongariro, Ngauruhoe, and Ruapehu. Active faults (upthrown to west) trend away from viewer in centre and right foreground, and Ketetahi Springs are visible on the north side of Tongariro. *Photo: S.N. Beatus*

tsunamis have been reported as reaching New Zealand, but no major damage ensued. An early warning system is established.

Flooding is a hazard that, although not strictly due to geological activity, can be assessed with the help of geological evidence. River flood plains give clues as to the extent of past floods, before rivers were affected and channelled by man's activities. Although most rivers prone to seasonal flooding are now controlled by stopbanks, the banks are usually only high enough to contain normally expected floods. There will always be the extraordinary flood which will breach the stopbank and take the river back to its old flood plain. Indeed, where a river is confined it may actually build up its bed within the stopbanks so that unless dredged, less water is required to top the bank. Where there is geological evidence of flooding before European settlement, it is prudent to site buildings and structures on higher ground.

Acknowledgments

The map was compiled mainly from published information, primarily the Geological map of New Zealand 1 : 1 000 000 and the Quaternary geology of New Zealand 1 : 1 000 000. I am grateful to many officers of the Geological Survey who willingly gave their time to comment on early drafts of the map and to supply me with recent unpublished information, in particular Dr P. B. Andrews who supplied a map of the Chatham Islands. The text was compiled from a multitude of sources, in particular the Geology of New Zealand (1978), and I am indebted to Messrs K. R. Berryman, L. J. Brown, H. J. Campbell, L. E. Oborn, A. M. Sherwood, B. N. Thompson; Drs R. L. Brathwaite, R. A. Cooper, J. I. Raine, and R. P. Suggate; and Mrs E. Tiller for their comments and improvements. Especial thanks to Messrs D. A. Francis and D. W. Heron for thoughtful and thorough editing, and to Mr D. L. Homer and Ms W. St. George for providing the many fine photographs in the text. I gratefully acknowledge the support, encouragement, and helpful comments throughout the project, of Drs I. G. Speden and D. G. Bishop. Thanks are due to Mrs A. Willoughby and F. Tonks for patient typing, and to the cartographers of Science Mapping Unit and editors of Science Information Publishing Centre for their skill and expertise in the production and publication of this work.

Suggested further reading and references

Forsyth, P. J. 1985: A beginners guide to New Zealand rocks and minerals. Wellington, New Zealand. Government Printer. 44 p.

Gage, M. 1980: Legends in the rocks, an outline of New Zealand geology. Christchurch, Whitcoulls. 426 p.

Lillie, A. R. 1980: Strata and structure in New Zealand. Auckland, Tohunga Press. 441 p.

Molloy, L. F. (compiler) 1980: Land alone endures. *Department of Scientific and Industrial Research discussion paper no. 3.* 284 p.

Stevens, G. R. 1980: New Zealand adrift. Wellington, A. H. & A. W. Reed. 442 p.

Stevens, G. R. 1985: Lands in collision: Discovering New Zealand's past geography. *DSIR information series no. 161.* 129 p.

Suggate, R. P.; Riddolls, P. M. 1976: Geology. Pp. 90–95 in Wards, I. McL. *ed.*: New Zealand atlas. Wellington, New Zealand. Government Printer. 292 p.

Suggate, R. P.; Stevens, G. R.; Te Punga, M. T. *ed.* 1978: The geology of New Zealand. Wellington, New Zealand. Government Printer. 2 vols, 820 p.

Thompson, B. N. 1976: Mineral resources. Pp. 154–156 in Wards, I. McL. *ed.*: New Zealand atlas. Wellington, New Zealand. Government Printer. 292 p.

Thornton, J. 1985: Field guide to New Zealand geology. Auckland, Reed Methuen. 226 p.

Williams, G. J. 1974: Economic geology of New Zealand. 2nd ed. *Australasian Institute of Mining and Metallurgy monograph series 4.*

Information on the geology of New Zealand has appeared in 3 monograph series and 4 map series published by the Department of Scientific and Industrial Research. The monograph series are:

New Zealand Geological Survey bulletins
DSIR bulletins
DSIR information series

Many early works are out of print. Information concerning titles and availability can be found in the Publications list, obtainable from Science Information Publishing Centre, DSIR, P.O. Box 9741, Wellington, New Zealand.

The map series published for the New Zealand Geological Survey, DSIR, are:

Geological map of New Zealand series
New Zealand Geological Survey industrial series
New Zealand Geological Survey urban series
New Zealand Geological Survey miscellaneous series

Lists of available maps may be obtained from the Publications Officer, New Zealand Geological Survey, P.O. Box 30-368, Lower Hutt, New Zealand.

Glossary

andesite Fine grained, medium coloured volcanic rock which contains the feldspar mineral andesine. It is an intermediate rock with 52–66% silica content.

anticline An upfolded structure (see Fig. 34).

argillite A hard compact sedimentary rock composed of mud- or silt-sized particles.

aureole A zone in the host rock surrounding an igneous intrusion, of which the composition has been changed by heat and fluid from the molten intrusion.

basalt Fine grained, dark coloured volcanic rock. It is a basic rock with less than 50% silica content.

batholith A large body of igneous rock that has been intruded as molten magma into high levels of the earth's crust.

bedding plane A plane between two layers of sediment of similar or differing composition. The planes are parallel to one another at distances ranging from a few millimetres to several metres apart.

bentonite Light coloured, soft, plastic, porous variety of clay with the ability to absorb water resulting in a vast increase in volume.

bituminous coal Black coal with bright shining lustre, low moisture, and high carbon content and heating value.

breccia Sedimentary rock formed of angular rock fragments of any size, of the same or differing composition.

chert Sedimentary rock of chemical origin, composed mainly of silica with no visible grains. Generally very hard.

concretion Hard generally calcareous body of sediment of any size, and generally rounded in shape (commonly subspherical), occurring as a discrete unit within softer sediment. Commonly aligned in rows along bedding planes.

conglomerate Sedimentary rock formed of rounded rock fragments larger than 2 mm of the same or differing compositions in a finer grained matrix (see Fig. 17, 24).

coquina Sedimentary rock composed entirely of loosely cemented shell fragments (limestone), (see Fig. 46).

dacite Fine grained, light coloured volcanic rock. An acid rock with over 66% silica content.

dike Tabular band of intrusive rock that cuts across structure of host rock (see Fig. 31).

diorite Coarse grained plutonic rock with many dark coloured minerals. An intermediate rock with between 50 and 66% silica content.

dolerite Fine to medium grained, dark coloured plutonic rock, with less than 50% silica content (basic). Generally occurs as dikes.

dunite Plutonic rock composed almost entirely of the mineral olivine, named after Dun Mountain in Nelson. An ultrabasic rock.

fault Zone of fracture in rock along which there has been movement. The movement may range from a few centimetres to many hundreds of kilometres.

gabbro Coarse grained basic plutonic rock with dark coloured minerals predominant and less than 45% silica content.

gneiss High grade metamorphic rock, of generally banded, coarse grained appearance (see Fig. 16).
  quartzofeldspathic indicates the presence of the minerals quartz and feldspar in equal amounts.
  feldspathic indicates the predominance of feldspar over quartz.
  amphibolite facies indicates the presence of amphibole minerals such as hornblende.
  granulite facies indicates a certain texture rather than mineral content. The grains are equi-dimensional and interlocking. This is a very high grade metamorphic rock.

granite Coarse grained light coloured plutonic rock with more than 66% silica content (acid).

granodiorite Coarse grained, medium coloured plutonic rock with more than 66% silica, and plagioclase as the dominant feldspar.

greensand Sandstone containing considerable amounts of the mineral glauconite.

greywacke (1) Hard sedimentary rock composed of sand-sized particles comprising quartz, feldspar and rock fragments.
(2) Popular term for alternating sequences of greywacke sandstone and argillite (see Fig. 27).

ignimbrite Rock composed of volcanic fragments welded together; generally acidic (more than 66% silica content).

joint A fracture within sedimentary or igneous rocks, which has formed either during consolidation of sediment or by subsequent stress. Joints are commonly seen in sets, cutting each other at regular angles (see Fig. 13).

keratophyre Volcanic rock containing the feldspar albite. An acid rock with more than 66% silica content.

lignite Compact, bedded, carbonaceous deposit with plant fragments clearly visible; has high moisture, and low carbon contents. Commonly known as brown coal.

limestone Sedimentary rock with over 50% calcium carbonate content. May be directly crystallised from sea water, composed of shells and skeletons of organisms, as in coral reefs, or be calcareous detritus cemented together.

loess Very fine grained sediment deposited by wind action.

magma Molten rock deep within the earth's crust, providing the lava for volcanic eruptions, and which may be intruded en masse into higher crustal levels.

melange A unit of chaotically mixed blocks of rocks of differing composition, origin and size, within a sheared fine grained matrix.

mudstone Sedimentary rock made up of mud- or silt-sized particles.

orogeny Period of mountain building.

peridotite Coarse grained plutonic rock of very dark green colour, composed predominantly of olivine and containing very little silica; an ultrabasic rock.

porphyry Plutonic rock which contains crystals of one mineral which are larger than any of the surrounding minerals.

pumice Light coloured, glassy, perforated volcanic rock, containing more than 66% silica. The numerous cavities make it very lightweight.

quartzite Very hard sedimentary rock composed predominantly of quartz grains.

rhyolite Fine grained or glassy, light coloured volcanic rock containing the mineral potash feldspar and with more than 66% silica content (acid).

sandstone Sedimentary rock composed of sand-sized particles.

schist Metamorphic rock with a streaky appearance, caused by closely parallel mineral layering.

scoria Dark coloured, perforated, slightly crystalline volcanic rock, of basaltic or andesitic origin. Has a rubbly texture, and commonly forms cones.

serpentinite Altered igneous or metamorphic rock, composed of the mineral serpentine; generally has dark green, lustrous, non-crystalline appearance.

shale Sedimentary rock, composed of mud-sized particles, which is finely laminated (i.e., numerous partings parallel to bedding).

siliceous Containing abundant silica.

slate Hard, slightly metamorphosed mudstone with prominent parallel fracture planes.

spilite Fine grained, dark coloured, volcanic rock (altered basalt), containing the mineral albite feldspar, and less than 50% silica content. It commonly exhibits "pillow" structures (see Fig. 14).

sub-bituminous coal Black coal with faint brown tinge, and dull shine. Moderate moisture content, carbon content, and heating value.

syncline A downfold structure (see Frontispiece).

tectonic Pertaining to movement of the earth's crust.

till Debris carried within, on top of, and pushed in front of a glacier, and deposited on its retreat.

tuff A bedded sedimentary deposit composed of volcanic ash.

unconformity A break in the geological record, usually resulting in an angular discordance between strata.

volcanogenic Of volcanic origin, for example, sediments derived from volcanic rocks.

Index

V. R. WARD, GOVERNMENT PRINTER, WELLINGTON, NEW ZEALAND—1987

INSIDE...

KU-473-111

Published 2019.
Little Brother Books, Ground Floor, 23 Southernhay East, Exeter, Devon, EX1 1QL
Printed in Poland.
books@littlebrotherbooks.co.uk | www.littlebrotherbooks.co.uk

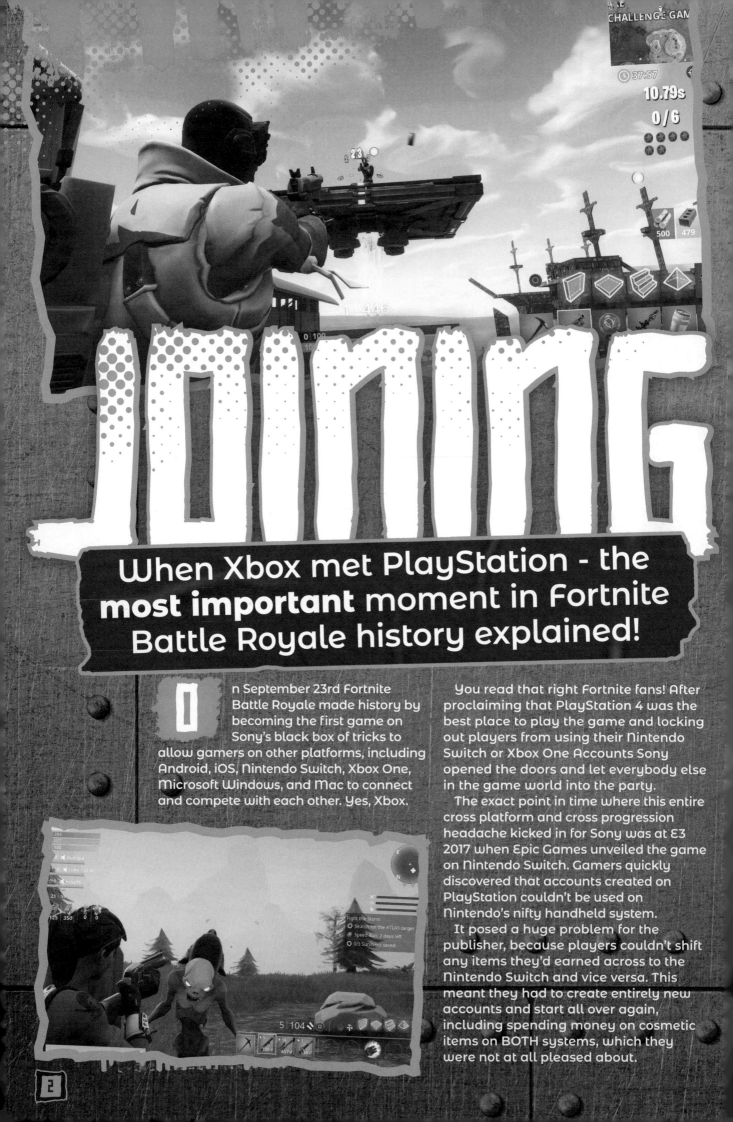

JOINING

When Xbox met PlayStation - the **most important** moment in Fortnite Battle Royale history explained!

On September 23rd Fortnite Battle Royale made history by becoming the first game on Sony's black box of tricks to allow gamers on other platforms, including Android, iOS, Nintendo Switch, Xbox One, Microsoft Windows, and Mac to connect and compete with each other. Yes, Xbox.

You read that right Fortnite fans! After proclaiming that PlayStation 4 was the best place to play the game and locking out players from using their Nintendo Switch or Xbox One Accounts Sony opened the doors and let everybody else in the game world into the party.

The exact point in time where this entire cross platform and cross progression headache kicked in for Sony was at E3 2017 when Epic Games unveiled the game on Nintendo Switch. Gamers quickly discovered that accounts created on PlayStation couldn't be used on Nintendo's nifty handheld system.

It posed a huge problem for the publisher, because players couldn't shift any items they'd earned across to the Nintendo Switch and vice versa. This meant they had to create entirely new accounts and start all over again, including spending money on cosmetic items on BOTH systems, which they were not at all pleased about.

Those last four words - select third party content - are vitally important to gamers the world over. Why? Because it sounds like Fortnite may have just opened the floodgates for a whole host of games to be added to the cross platform roster.

Imagine a world where you can play FIFA, Call of Duty, Battlefield, Street Fighter or WWE with friends on Nintendo Switch, Xbox One, Microsoft Windows, and Mac? That would

FORCES

be awesome! Epic Games is busy working on an Account Merge feature, which would allow Fortnite players with multiple console-linked accounts to transfer Battle Royale purchases, records, V-Bucks, and Save the World campaign access. However, due to some teething problems the feature hasn't been released at the time of going to press. Here's hoping that the developer resolves these very soon! Either way, the future is bright for cross-platform play between PlayStation 4 owners and gamers the world over!

By locking players out it looked bad for Sony and for PlayStation, so it was a huge relief to fans of Fortnite Battle Royale that the publisher and developer lifted the ban and sent the game world into a tailspin. This is a huge deal for players, and not just of Fortnite Battle Royale. But before we talk about why, it's important to note that it was Epic Games' behemoth title that was no doubt solely responsible for this new shift in policy.

It's arguably the most popular game in the world, and it was quite clear that the unique progression mechanics and in-game purchases were what forced Sony to change its mind and allow gamers to share. In announcing the new feature Sony stated that, "Following a comprehensive evaluation process, SIE has identified a path toward supporting cross-platform features for select third party content."

STAY FROSTY

Diving into the ice cool Fortnite Deep Freeze bundle.

In late 2018 Epic Games and Warner Bros. Interactive teamed up to release a super cool Fortnite exclusive console edition on PlayStation 4, Xbox One and Nintendo Switch. The bundle, which hit retail shelves across the nation back in November, included a whole heap of goodies for players and will set you back £24.99 on all three formats at the time of going to press.

The box includes an install of Fortnite Battle Royale if you haven't already got it downloaded onto your machine. It does not include a copy of Fortnite Save The World, which will cost you extra. At the time of going to press The Standard Founders Pack costs between £32.99 and £34.99 on PlayStation Store and Xbox Games Store, whereas the Deluxe edition costs £49.99 on both game stores.

DEEP FREEZE BUNDLE CONTAINS

FORTNITE BATTLE ROYALE GAME

FROSTBITE SKIN + CHILL-AXE

COLD FRONT GLIDER

FREEZING POINT BACK BLING

1,000 V-BUCKS

INTERNET CONNECTION REQUIRED. DOWNLOAD CODE ONLY.

Next up is 1000 V-Bucks, more than enough to cover a single Battle Pass. The Battle Passes are released at the start of every season in Fortnite Battle Royale, and work on two tiers - silver and gold, with silver being free and gold requiring you to purchase the Battle Pass at the start of each new season for 950 V-Bucks.

Alongside the V-Bucks and the install of Fortnite Battle Royale there is also a Legendary Skin called Frostbit, which also features the Freezing Point Back Bling, Cold Front Glider and Chill-Axe Harvesting Tool. It's a slick set and ideal for anyone looking to jump into Fortnite Battle Royale for the first time, especially with the addition of the V-Bucks, which allows you to purchase a Battle Pass.

The Deep Freeze bundle is available on store shelves now, but if you don't feel like taking a walk to shops you can purchase it via the PlayStation, Nintendo and Xbox Game Stores. However, if you are playing Fortnite Save The World it's worth noting that items in the Deep Freeze Bundle are not cross transferable.

Animal Antics

Meet the cuddly, cute and **scary Pets** of Fortnite Battle Royale!

Ever wanted to drop into a Fortnite Battle Royale match with a dog or dragon strapped to your back? Well now you can with the Fortnite Pets Back Bling! These cuddly critters were rumoured to be appearing in the game for a while, so it was a huge deal for fans of the game when they launched back in September 2018. It meant Players could dive into battle on the Fortnite Island with an animal on their back ready to kick some serious butt, and look super cool doing it!

Furry Back Bling

Fortnite Pets are Back Bling, so that means they're unlocked and equipped in Fortnite Battle Royale like any other Back Bling or character dressing. Of course the difference here is that these cuddly little rascals actually react to what's going on around you during a match. The Pets were included with the Season Six Battle Pass, and each one came with a selection of colours the further along you progressed.

Own 'Em All!

Owners of the Season Six Battle Pass really had to work to earn

these creatures, but boy was it worth it! At Level 12 on the Battle Pass Gold Tier Bonsey The Dog became available. Level 29 brought it with Camo The Chameleon and Level 43 landed Players the chance to carry Scales The Dragon into a 100-player brawl. As Players progressed through the Season Six Battle Pass by completing challenges additional colours became available, including a black Scales The Dragon and a Mocha Bonesy The Dog.

What Do They Do?!

They do absolutely nothing, Fortnite fans! The Pets are simply nothing more than cosmetic items exactly like other Back Bling that can be unlocked or purchased in the game. Cosmetic items such as these have no impact on the game; they're simply a style choice, and a way to jazz up your character's look in battle. But who cares, because they're cuddly pets and they look really awesome, people!

Safe And Sound

One of the biggest concerns Fortnite fans had when the Pets were announced was what exactly happened to these cute animals when an opposing player knocked them out of a match. We're here to tell you that all is well – the Pets simply spend a moment or two looking around, wondering what happened and then simply disappear into the ether until you bring them back for another match!

WILD, WILD, WEST

Take a trip back in time with Fortnite Battle Royale's new Limited Time Mode!

"This town ain't big enough for the hundred of us!" so said the patched notes for his cowboy flavoured slice of action that Epic Games rolled out right around the time Rockstar Games' Red Dead Redemption was breaking sales records on PlayStation 4 and Xbox One consoles.

The developers were smart enough to realise the hoopla that would surround the launch of one the biggest games of the year and in order to ensure Fortnite fans stayed put, they cooked up this western Limited Time Mode, and boy is it a heck of a lot of fun to play around with! ●

Kaboom!

One of the biggest additions to the game with the Wild West Limited Time Mode is Dynamite. It packs one hell of a bang, dealing out 70 damage points if it hits another player, and 800 damage points to structures. That means, if you're hiding out in a self-made structure and someone's hurling Dynamite your way you'd better bail out of there as quickly as possible, because it's coming down!

Nice Shootin' Tex

Considering this Limited Time Mode is set in Frontier Times it's only fitting that some of the more modern and futuristic weaponry is culled whenever you dive in. The only guns you'll wield throughout a match are Hunting Rifles, Pump Shotguns, Double Barrel Shotguns, Six Shooters and, on occasion, the awesome Mini-gun. With weapons like this it means you're going to have to get up close and personal the majority of the time, so you'd better be sure of two things – one: you're a damn good shot, and two: you keep that weapon loaded at all times!

Drink Up, Cowboy!

Shield Potions are an essential gameplay component in Fortnite Battle Royale, but in Wild West Limited Time Mode they've been cut too, and instead you're left to dash around the map hunting down containers of Slurp Juice to refill defences. Remember, Slurp Juice takes a little time to get down the hatch, so watch your back while you chug one of those bad boys!

Cozy Campfire

Another way to heal up during battle is with the addition of Cozy Campfires. They are extremely useful in battle, because they don't just heal you, they also heal teammates, so if you have one and your squad is running low on health drop it in!

SAVING THE WORLD AIN'T FREE

Fortnite **Save The World** free-to-play has been delayed. Let's find out why!

Before we get into the reasons why Fortnite Save The World is not currently free (despite Epic Games telling fans this would be the case in 2018) on consoles and PC, let's take a look at how it works in comparison to Fortnite's Battle Royale mode, as well as what you get for your hard earned money if you do decide to go ahead and pay for it, before it goes free-to-play sometime in 2019.

What is save the world?

It was released in July of 2017 and is a co-operative play survival game where you team up with three other players to battle waves of zombie-like enemies. It's got pretty much all the ingredients that make the Battle Royale mode so great, including shooting and building, as well as elements of tower defence. It was created and developed by Epic Games and People Can Fly, the team behind Bulletstorm and Gears of War: Judgement.

There are multiple versions of the game, including the Standard edition, Deluxe Edition, Super Deluxe Edition and Limited Edition. Prices vary from platform to platform, but keep an eye out for discounts because Epic is always slashing the price to encourage new players to join the fight against the marauding zombies!

When will it be free?

Anyway, onto the big, burning question – when will it be free to all players like Fortnite Battle Royale? Right now, dates are hazy, but Epic Games is working on a whole host of features for it in order to ensure the transition is smooth and simple. Here's what the team said back in late 2018 when it decided to hold off on releasing the new model of Fortnite Save The World.

"We're working on a broad set of features, reworks, and backend system scaling we believe are needed to go free-to-play. 'Save the World' has grown consistently since our launch in July 2017 and Fortnite overall has experienced unprecedented growth. Scaling up for the legions of player heroes who will be joining the fight is key to providing an excellent experience. This applies to all of our players, old and new, so we're taking the time to get this right."

Here's hoping the team get these features in place relatively quickly so Fortnite fans the world over can start enjoying this very cool mode – FOR FREE!

SMASH!

Everything you need to know about Quadcrashers in Fortnite Battle Royale!

The team at Epic Games are always adding new and fun stuff to Fortnite Battle Royale, and Quadcrashers are arguably one of the most enjoyable vehicle additions to the game so far. They're fast, furious and can bust through just about anything when hit with at high speed. To really master these new machines you need to know how they work on the battlefield, so let's take a look at them.

Jump on!

Quadcrashers can seat up to two players at a time, so if you're playing Duos and grab one of these be sure to honk the horn to get your teammates' attention so they can jump aboard and ride with you to different areas of the map.

Parking Spots

You can find Quadcrashers all over the map. Locations include Risky Reels, Retail Row, Salty Springs and Greasy Grove. And this is just a small selection of spots they're dotted around. Chances are wherever you go you'll find one!

Race Day!

If you feel like trying something other than shooting people grab yourself a Quadcrasher and head to the east of Junk Junction where you'll find a racetrack, which lets you compete in timed races using the newly created vehicles. Vroom!

Engine Problems

Quadcrashers are LOUD so don't barrel into the middle of a chaotic shootout between other players, because they will hear you coming a mile away and blast you to kingdom come. Either ditch the vehicle or boost it as fast as you can!

Hit 'n' Run

The Quadcrashers are designed to smash through structures thanks to their heavy-duty construction, so use them to burst across the battlefield and smash down enemies in structures, or to ram through walls to take out players on the other side.

Rough Landing

Quadcrashers may be tough, but that doesn't mean they'll protect you if you do something daft like speed off the edge of a cliff and land awkwardly at the bottom. Doing that will result in your character taking damage, so be careful!

Air Time

Like the ATV in previous updates, one of the most enjoyable things to do with the Quadcrasher is to build ramps and boost off them to catch some serious air. Just make sure you nail that landing or it's going to sting, folks – a hell of a lot!

Flyboy

Ever wanted to see what another player looks like soaring through the air? Then grab yourself a Quadcrasher, hit the boost button and find some enemies on the battlefield. Once you hit them the vehicle will send them flying sky high!

SLICK SKINS!

There are so many great skins to choose from in Fortnite Battle Royale it's impossible to list every single one of them here. If we wanted to do that it would probably take an entire book! That said, some skins are just so cool they need to be added to your collection, so without further ado we've put together a collection of some of the best ones that have appeared on the Fortnite Battle Royale Store to date. Just remember, skins cost money so choose wisely before spending your hard earned pocket money on deciding which one fits your avatar best!

Patch Patroller

If you like spooky skins then you'll want to grab this Patch Patroller that was released as part of a Halloween themed pack in 2018. A masked vigilante in a black and orange getup, this guy is guaranteed to strike fear into your opponents!

Jack Gourdon

Clearly a bit of a nod to The Nightmare Before Christmas, Jack Gourdon comes clad in a black tux covered in a series of Halloween lanterns. He's both stylish and spooky in equal measure, making him one of our favourite new skins out there.

Deadfire

The Wild West comes to Fortnite Battle Royale with Deadfire, a seriously cool cowboy kitted out in slick duster, cowboy hat and the Shackled Stone Back Bling that causes the character to emit spectral flames after a certain number of kills.

Brainiac

No, it's not the villain from Superman (but it could be!). This uncommon skin features a soldier with strange green skin, an army vest and red neck scarf. Released right before the annual Halloween event, many believe he's a zombie!

Hay Man

Eek! If you see this terrifying skin coming at you wielding a gun you'd better run! Hay Man is designed to look like a scarecrow come to life, and boy it works! He's got glowing red eyes, bird skull necklace and bird's nest as his Back Bling.

Valkyrie

This Legendary female skin is one of the most awesome to appear in the game so far. Culled from the world of Norse mythology, Valkyrie comes kitted out in reinforced steel, spiked helmet and glowing eyes that burn with bright blue flames.

NightShade

Be mysterious. Be a Tomatohead! This slick chick comes clad in an all-black suit that closely resembles outfits we've seen before such as cover field agents and assassins. She's part of the Pizza Pit set that included a delivery bag and pizza cutter.

Stage Slayer

It's Slash from Guns 'N' Roses! Actually, no it isn't, but we're pretty certain the team at Epic were thinking of him when they designed this new skin that features a rock star in top hat and black sunglasses, and is part of the Garage Band set.

Wukong

Inspired by Monkey King, one of the greatest ever stories from Chinese mythology, Wukong comes dressed in mighty Chinese-styled armour and is part of the Wukong set that includes the Jingu Bang Harvesting Tool and Royale Flags.

Sushi Master

Do you like sushi with your guns? We do! Sushi Master is a Rare skin that comes with an avatar dressed as a traditional Japanese Sushi Chef. The cool thing about this skin is that if you snag it you unlock the Chef's Choice Back Bling.

Overtaker

Now this is definitely one of the coolest costumes we've seen in recent updates. Just look at this guy in his white racing jacket, trousers and racing helmet. Once you nab this skin you can grab the Lane Splitter Back Bling with samurai sword!

The Ace

Part of the sticky fingered Getaway Gang set, but only available to anyone who purchased the Fortnite Battle Royale Start Pack #3 at the time of going to press, The Ace comes with the Cuff Case Back Bling and Crowbar Harvesting Tool.

Beef Boss

Part of the Durr Burger Set, Beef Boss is terrifying thanks to his hamburger head and weirdly long tongue! We know it's part of a Halloween Set, but if we saw this on the battlefield it'd send us running off in the opposite direction. Scary stuff!

Sun Tan Specialist

Time to hit the beach with Sun Tan Specialist, a hip looking lifeguard complete with shorts, flip flops, sunglasses, suntan lotion and, if you want to complete the outfit, the Rescue Ring Back Bling. He's the perfect reminder of how much we love summer!

Wreck Raider

The Wreck Raider is an Epic skin clad in full scuba gear, and despite the fact he's wearing flippers he moves around the map just fine in Fortnite Battle Royale. Now, be warned – this skin DOES NOT allow you to swim underwater just in case you had any ideas!

Vertex

Vertex is badass, and definitely one of the more striking skins to choose from on the Fortnite Battle Royale Store. Featuring full-body armour, helmet and the Deflector Back Bling, Vertex is part of the Apex Protocol Set released last year.

Dusk

Dusk is a really cool, villainous character that came as part of the Nite Coven Set during Season 6 of Fortnite Battle Royale. She sported wicked looking blood red eyes and white hair, and you could also kit her out with Dusk Wings Back Bling.

Giddy-Up

This weird and whacky outfit featured a character riding a Loot Llama. Yes, really! It also had a pair of fake legs, which looked completely bonkers and will have your opponents in stitches right before you blast them into oblivion for the win!

DJ Yonder

Pump up the volume on the battlefield with DJ Yonder, an epic skin released alongside the Season 6 Battle Pass. This cool dude comes in a green suit and a zany mask shaped like a robot llama that reflects light just like a disco ball.

Bunnymoon

Bunnymoon is an uncommon female skin that features a slick character clad in a purple and black striped top with combat pants wrapped up in what look like Christmas tree lights. She didn't come with any bonus items, but she's still cool!

Spider Knight

Whoa! Spider Knight is one scary skin that's for sure, and we certainly wouldn't want to meet this guy on the battlefield in the dark of night. Clad in a spooky spider themed helmet with leather jacket and dagger, he came as part of the Arachnid set.

Arachne

Also arriving as part of the Arachnid set, Arachne arrived during the Halloween season of 2018 sporting a black and leather vest, super skinny leather trousers, gauntlets and one of the coolest looking helmets in the game. Oh, and spider Back Bling!

Airheart

Released as part of the Aviation set that included the Exhaust skydiving trail and Dirigible glider skin, this red haired female character was clearly a nod to the legendary aviation pioneer, Amelia Earhart. To complete the set you could also grab the Airflow Back Bling.

Grill Sergeant

Part of the Durr Burger set, the Grill Sergeant came kitted out in a fast food employee garb that included a hat and apron. One of the funniest items he came equipped with if you went for the complete getup was the Patty Whacker Harvesting Tool.

Sanctum

Sanctum wants to suck your blood! Well, at least we think that's what this creepy vampire themed skin is thinking with his red eyes, huge claws and pale white skin! Part of the Nite Coven set alongside Dusk, Sanctum hit the Fortnite Store just in time for Halloween 2018.

ROYAL RUMBLE

It's all out war in Fortnite Battle Royale's **Team Rumble** Limited Time Mode!

T he team at Epic Games sure do know how to treat their fans. They're constantly cooking up wild and whacky modes to keep players engaged should they feel like taking a break from the usual Battle Royale Mode. Enter Team Rumble Limited Time Mode, introduced in Fortnite 6.31 released back in November 2018. This kick-ass new way to play ramps up the action tenfold, and is far more aggressive than the Game Modes you're more accustomed to in Fortnite Battle Royale.

Attack, Attack, Attack!

Team Rumble Limited Time Mode is incredibly fast-paced, pitting two teams of 20 players against each other. The goal is simple; players need to work with teammates to wrack up 100 kills to win the match and grab that Victory Royale. Essentially this is a race; a race with guns, bombs and anything else that comes to hand as you wade through waves of enemies vying to take you down for a point.

Re-Animated

One of the great things about Team Rumble Limited Time Mode is that players respawn once eliminated during a match. It takes just five seconds for you to wind up back on the battlefield, so you're unlikely to miss out on much of the action. But remember, if a member of the opposing team takes you

out they're awarded a point. If that team reaches max points it means game over, Fortnite fan!

Inventory Bonuses

Another difference between this Limited Time Mode and the other Game Modes in Fortnite Battle Royale is that if you're eliminated you get to keep everything in your inventory. That way you're not wasting time running around looking for weapons once you respawn on the map. If you're the one doing the eliminating the Players you wipe out will spawn everything from ammo to building materials.

KaBlam!

Uncommon weapons and

weapons of a higher rarity spawn more frequently in Team Rumble Limited Time Mode too. These dish out a substantial amount of damage, which means you're likely to notch quite a few kills if you can master 'em. The better weaponry also encourages Players to be a little more daring; don't be afraid to barrel in there and hunt down opposing players for team points! But don't get too cocky, because it's important to stick with your team to work together if you want to nab that all-important Victory Royale. Being a Lone Wolf can be pretty dangerous in this hectic Game Mode, so watch yourself out there! ●

POP, POP, POP!

Balloon 101

Balloons are an Epic Rarity, and come in packs of 20. Six can be inflated at a time using Primary and Secondary Fire Buttons to inflate and release them. Each balloon only stays inflated for a certain amount of time, so remember that!

Everything you need to know about Balloons, the new and super exciting mode of transport in Fortnite Battle Royale!

There are so many ways of getting around in Fortnite Battle Royale, including vehicles and Gliders, but here's one we DID NOT expect to arrive in an update back in November 2018 – Balloons! Despite what you might think Balloons are extremely versatile and can be used in a variety of ways to gain the lead on the battlefield. Here are some tips and tricks to help you master them in the game.

Where To Find Them

Even though Balloons are labelled as an Epic Rarity class they're actually pretty easy to find. Packs of them are dotted around the map as Ground Loot, and they're also hidden inside Loot Chests as well as Supply Drops and Loot Llamas.

Silent & Deadly

Balloons are the only way of getting around silently in Fortnite Battle Royale. If you find a pack during a match you can use them to float into the air and sneak up on enemy structures, or infiltrate heavily populated buildings via the rooftops.

How High?

While you may be tempted to inflate Balloons and float your way to the clouds we would suggest erring on the side of caution – once you've reached a certain height they'll pop and send you plummeting to the ground. So be careful, folks!

Shoot 'Em!

If you're on the ground and spot an opponent sailing through the skies using Balloons you can shoot them. If they don't have any replacement ones you'll snag yourself a kill, but don't forget that players can do the same thing to you!

Up & Down

To increase the speed of Balloon ascension all you have to do is inflate more until you've reached your max amount. To drop down steadily to an area on the battlefield simply let go of the Balloons and sail down comfortably to the ground.

Keep Count!

When using Balloons in Fortnite Battle Royale it's definitely worth keeping an eye on how many you have in your inventory. If you're flying too high they will pop, so if you don't have enough left you're likely to fall to the ground and get eliminated.

No Weapons

One of the most important things to remember when using Balloons is that you are extremely vulnerable up there in the air and can't use a weapon, because the Primary and Secondary Fire Buttons are used for controlling ascent and descent.

THE BIG BANG

Ditch bullets for bombs in Fortnite Battle Royale's **High Explosives** Limited Time mode!

If you thought standard Fortnite Battle Royale matches were wild, then wait until you get a load of High Explosives Limited Time Mode! Brawls are still 100 player battles, but the twist here is that anything bullet related has been stripped away, and all that remains are things that go BOOM on the crazy Fortnite Island. That means you'll be grabbing rocket launchers, grenade launchers, remote explosives as well as dynamite at loot drops, and using them to down opponents.

Loot Drops

One of the great things about this Limited Time Mode is that Loot Drops are far more frequent, so be sure to keep an eye out for them as they appear in the sky. Once you spot one, be

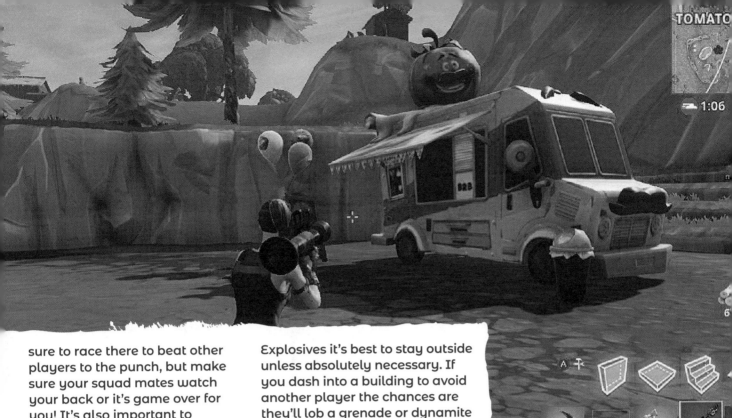

sure to race there to beat other players to the punch, but make sure your squad mates watch your back or it's game over for you! It's also important to remember that those of you prone to headshots with high-powered sniper rifles need to change up your play style. High Explosives is all about shooting from the hip. Don't waste time lining up a shot or you'll die – fast!

Stay Outside

Given that explosives are the primary weapons in High

Explosives it's best to stay outside unless absolutely necessary. If you dash into a building to avoid another player the chances are they'll lob a grenade or dynamite your way and if you're caught in the blast radius you'll be taken out. You can use staircases and walls to your advantage, but be prepared to take some damage when anything goes bang!

Jump Around

Just like in the standard Battle Royale Mode one of the most effective ways to avoid getting blown to smithereens is by leaping around the map, especially when facing down another player. Yes, it makes it that bit harder to pull off the perfect shot and take out an opponent, but bouncing around will help you avoid taking a rocket to the face.

Sneaky, Sneaky

A really effective way of taking out enemies in High Explosives Limited Time Mode is by planting remote explosives in areas containing Loot Chests, then finding a good spot to hide before waiting for a player to arrive on scene. Once they do hit that detonator and watch them disappear off the map for good! Oh, and remember – don't open the Loot Chest otherwise it runs the sneak attack! ●

High Explosives

Battle Royale

Drop In & Load Up
Pick a landing spot and search for gear.

Stay Inside the Eye of the Storm
Deadly clouds are closing in. The Eye will shrink as the storm intensifies.

'Splode the Enemies
Send them all back to the lobby to earn the Victory Royale.

LOADING

Use the map to see where you are, and where the storm is headed.

MAP MADNESS

Take a trip to these picturesque **new locations** on the Fortnite Island map!

The Fortnite map is without doubt one of the most constantly evolving game worlds in the history of videogames. Epic Games is constantly looking for new and inventive ways to keep things fresh not just in terms of gameplay, but in how it reshapes huge chunks of the Fortnite Island map that players spend so much time on. Let's take a look at some of the most recent changes to the battlefield!

Loot Lake

Loot Lake has gone through quite a lot of changes since Fortnite Battle Royale began. First Kevin the Cube arrived, turning the water purple. Then there was the floating island high above it, and more recently it's been transformed into a Stonehenge-esque type location with lots of flowers and mini islands surrounding it.

Haunted Castle

Haunted Hills has always been quite the spooky location to drop into during a match, but it became even more frightening when Epic Games decided to drop a Haunted Castle into the mix! Explore it and you'll find a handful of Loot Chests, as well as creepy coffins! But don't blame us if you get scared, Fortnite Fans!

Frosty Flights

Looking for an X-4 Stormwing Plane to take to the skies in? Then drop into Frosty Flights, which first appeared at the start of Season 7 of Fortnite Battle Royale. Located in the south-western corner of the map, Frosty Flights is loaded with loot, plane hangars, houses and zip lines that lead to the chilly Polar Peak.

Polar Peak

Polar Peak can be found nestled in the centre of the winter wonderland that arrived during Season 7 of Fortnite Battle Royale. At the time of going to press it was the highest place on the Fortnite map. It's a cool place to venture to and soak up the snowy sight if you have some downtime in the multiplayer match.

Happy Hamlet

If you feel like taking a break from blasting opponents and fancy a little sight-seeing get yourself to the southern edge of the map to the west of Lucky Landing. There you'll find Happy Hamlet, a tiny, weeny European styled town. This place used to be Flush Factory, a serious drop-in hot spot for players!

Flush Factory

If you go looking for Flush Factory right now chances are you probably won't find it, because at the time of going to press the entire place was buried in snow. All that remains are the tips of buildings barely jutting out from underneath the white stuff. Next to it you'll find Happy Hamlet, which has replaced the rest of the area.

Frozen Lake

Remember Greasy Grove, the suburban neighbourhood over on the west side of the map? Well it's not there anymore, and instead there remains a huge frozen lake into which the buildings that once stood there have sunk. If you feel like it you can go for a quick skate around some of the old locations from days gone by.

DANCE OFF!
EMOTE ON **DANCE FLOORS** TO CAPTU
THEM FOR YOUR TEAM!

DISCO, DISCO, DISCO!

Boogie all night long on the battlefield in the Limited Time Mode, **Disco Domination.**

A rguably one of the most intriguing – and hilarious – Limited Time Modes to hit Fortnite Battle Royale since it's inception is Disco Domination. The mode is essentially a boogie-skewered take on the classic Domination modes that have appeared in the likes of Call of Duty and Battlefield games over the years.

How it works in Epic Games' version is quite simple: dance floors pop up all over the map, which you then travel to and clear off any other players. Once the coast is clear start dancing. Dance long enough and you'll capture the dance floor. Capture enough dance floors and fill your team's dance bar to 100 and you win!

THE **ENEMY** HAS TAKEN OVER ONE OF YOUR **DANCE FLOORS**!

Crash The Party

Now, if you're not the one doing the dancing and a rival team has already started boogying hard you might want to play it smart before diving in headfirst. If you have a scoped gun, pick a few enemies off from a distance. If you've rockets, send a few 'em their way to thin out the crowds, and then rush in there with your squad for the win.

Team Dance Off

The way Disco Domination works in terms of teams is by splitting up 100 players into two groups of 50, so you really need to work together with your squad mates to capture the dance floors and eliminate opposing players. Unlike in standard Battle Royale matches respawn is available during the Limited Time Mode, until the third and final Storm Eye has taken hold of the map, so keep an eye on it.

Loop It

While there are numerous dancing emotes to choose from in the game, the best ones to pick during Disco Domination are the ones that loop. Looping animations save you the hassle of opening the menu to keep repeating the same dance moves over and over until the dance floor has been captured.

Protect The Dance Floor

It's worth noting that you can't actually build on the dance floor when trying to take control of it, but what you can – and absolutely should – do is build some sort of protection around the area to avoid being picked off from a distance by a handful of opposing players brandishing high-powered sniper rifles. A good way to capture a dance floor quickly is to assign a teammate to building duties, while the rest of the squad dances to snag it.

THIS IS A STICK UP!

Hints and tips for mastering the Grappler in Fortnite Battle Royale.

Fortnite Battle Royale is already so much fun to play, but do you know what makes it even more ridiculously enjoyable? The addition of The Grappler - a nifty new gadget that has opened up a whole new world of traversal opportunities in skirmishes! Essentially, this thing turns your character into Spider-Man thanks to its abilities. It also changes the dynamic of battle big time – nowhere is safe now!

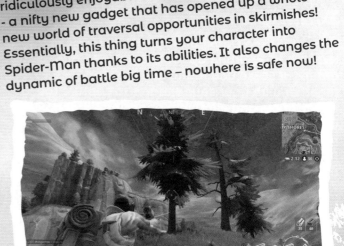

What is it?

The Grappler is a plunger that can be shot at any surface in the game world. Once it connects with the surface it yanks you towards the target area. It's essentially like having Spider-Man's web-shooting ability in Fortnite Battle Royale, and so much fun to play with.

M Is For Momentum

Shortly after The Grappler arrived Epic Games added a little something extra to its abilities with the momentum function. Now when firing it at a moving vehicle or another player you are rewarded with a speed boost as you hurtle towards them.

Limited Range

It's important to remember that range is limited when using The Grappler – it is just a length of rope tied to a plunger after all! It's easy to spot when not in range too – the target reticule will appear as an X.

Fast Mover

The Grappler has 15 shots in total, so you can move around super fast in certain situations once it's in your arsenal, but don't forget to keep an eye on how many you have left otherwise you could wind up staring down the sights of a gun.

Rush Mode

If you come across an enemy and they start blasting at you use The Grappler to zip towards them super quickly. This usually causes them to get disorientated, giving you enough time to switch to a weapon, take them out and grab a kill.

A Quick Escape

Sometimes things can get frantic in Fortnite Battle Royale, so having The Grappler to hand can be extremely useful in situations like these. If you're running low on health and someone is attacking just use it to flee the scene!

Height Advantage

Gaining a height advantage is essential to survival in Fortnite Battle Royale, and while building structures are key to this, so is The Grappler. If you need to check out an area from a vantage point use it to zip up a structure and scope the area.

Stealth Attack

If you spot an opponent high up on a structure picking off enemies from a distance use The Grappler to zip up to their location quietly while they're distracted and then take them out from behind with your weapon of choice!

Combo Attacks

The Grappler is excellent for pulling off killer combo attacks on enemies. To perform one of these you'll need a close range weapon in your arsenal, such as a shotgun. Simply zip to their location and blast them up close with your gun.

FORTNITE EVENTS

Take a deep dive into Fortnite Battle Royale's tournament system!

When Patch 6.10. for Fortnite Battle Royale hit gaming platforms it brought with it one of the most exciting new features of the game – Tournaments! These Events allowed gamers the world over to compete alongside and against some of the best Fortnite Battle Royale players. It was a huge moment for Fortnite, so let's take a look at some of the Events that took place over the last twelve months.

EVENT DETAILS

Practice Tournament Solo

The first Event to launch with the new game mode was a solo Event requiring players to score six points every match by taking out enemies. Players that nabbed a minimum of 20 points were rewarded with a pin.

Friday Night Fortnite

Friday Night Fortnite was a super fast and hectic squad-based mode that charged teams with scoring up to six points in a match, and earning at least 25 during a team session. Like the previous mode the reward was a cool in-game pin!

EVENT DETAILS

Practice Tournament Duos

This Duos Mode asked players to grab a gaming buddy and lead the charge against the rest of the world's Fortnite Battle Royale players by scoring 20 points minimum in exchange for another in-game pin over the course of three days.

Scavenger Pop-Up Cup Duos

The arrival of Scavenger Pop-Up Cup brought with it some cool treats for Fortnite Battle Royale fans. This tournament allowed Epic Games to test some new gameplay tweaks, including reduced materials and storm circle adjustments.

Winter Royale

The Winter Royale was without doubt the biggest Fortnite Battle Royale tournament to launch with the arrival of Events. Why? Players were competing to win one million dollars worth of prizes! Crazy stuff, right?!

Alchemist Pop-Up Cup Solo

The Alchemist Pop-Up Cup brought with it numerous gameplay adjustments to make the matches more interesting, as well as testing Limited Time Modes. The aim for players was to grab at least 20 points during the tournament for a pin.

GET CREATIVE!

Everything you need to know about Fortnite Battle Royale's **Creative Mode!**

Fortnite: Creative is probably one of the biggest and most interesting features ever to grace the world of Fortnite Battle Royale. What is it? We're glad you asked! Fortnite: Creative came with the arrival of Season 7 and is essentially a huge sandbox mode that allows you to create your own private island.

Yeah, it's awesome. In it you'll be able to invite your friends to play around and have as much fun as you want without worrying about other players trying to blast you back to the Start Menu. You can design everything from games, races, challenges and matches where you and your pals can duke it out against each other.

Let's take a look at how exactly Fortnite: Creative works!

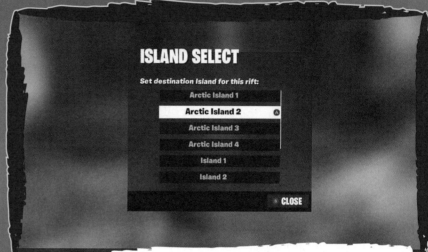

Player Islands

Player Islands are essentially blank slates for you to create stuff on from scratch. These creative spaces act like standalone servers and stay active for up to four hours at a time. You're allotted four islands, which allow you to mess around with different kinds of designs so that you can find one that works best for you.

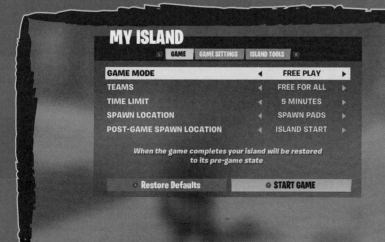

My Island Menu

The My Island Menu is really useful. To access it all you have to do is open up the Main Menu while you're messing around on your own personal island. Then simply look for the Game Tab, which will allow you to stop and start any crazy games you come up with or revert the island back to it's original game state.

Build your own Fortnite! Everything you do here is saved.

Make A Movie

The Replay function is one of the things we imagine Fortnite fans are going to have an absolute ball with in Fortnite: Creative. When playing in this unique mode the servers that host your island remain live for four hours, but what's really interesting is that all of your actions are recorded in 30-minute chunks and saved, so that if you pulled off an awesome stunt or takedown you can re-watch it!

Prefabs

Prefabs are pre-existing structures and will save you a whole heap of time. This menu is insanely big. There are so many structures for you to choose from to drop around the island, including chunks of Tilted Towers and some smaller less recognizable buildings. You can also add furniture, including fridges and shelves to buildings, so feel free to pack each to the gills with items for harvesting in fights.

Inventory Creation

The Creative Inventory is easily accessed from the Inventory Menu and lets you spawn everything from buildings to weaponry and in-game consumables. Heck, you can even craft Loot Chests and Loot Llamas and fill them with whatever you want! And because of this you can either be extremely generous or really tight with Loot and items to make matches easier or harder depending on play styles.

Memory Cap

This is one of the most important things to remember when playing around in Fortnite: Creative. The Memory Usage feature is Epic Games' attempt to stop servers being overloaded and crashing. The more players that jump into the world of Fortnite: Creative the less memory becomes available. At the time of going to press the Memory Usage is indicated by a bar at the bottom of the screen, so be sure to keep an eye out when playing with your Fortnite friends.

Let's Fly

Did we mention you are also able to fly in Fortnite: Creative? Well now you know! Flying allows you to move around the map at speed. It also helps when you want to build structures on different sections of the island at speed, but you can also whizz through the air during any battles you create and even shoot your opponents, which makes for some crazy fire-fight dynamics!

FOOD FIGHT

The fast food war to end all fast food wars comes to Fortnite Battle Royale!

Food Fight is without doubt one of the most popular Limited Time Modes to come to Fortnite Battle Royale since the game launched back in 2017. It pits two teams of 12 players against each other with both teams starting off on opposite sides of a huge wall that lowers after the countdown clock projected onto it reaches zero.

Tomato Heads

The twist is it's not just a race to eliminate the opposition, it's got a story too. The mode pits teams from rival fast food chains in the Fortnite universe against each other – namely Durr Burger and Pizza Pit. Players on the Durr Burger side have heads shaped like – you guessed it – hamburgers, while Pizza Pit warriors run around the map with Tomato Head, um, heads! It's crazy fun! Each team has to protect their mascot, so the trick is to use the ticking clock at

Our mascot's health is at 10 percent!

the outset of a match to build as much protection around it as quickly as possible.

Build Big

While the temptation may be to just grab as much loot as you can at the outset of a match, this is definitely the wrong approach. During our time on it we saw teams craft the most amazingly elaborate forts around mascots that boggled the mind. Loot is easy to come by in this mode, so don't fret. Always stay close to your team's fort and any time it looks like it's getting damaged start building extra defences around it, or you risk losing the

match if the mascot's health reaches zero.

Respawn

If you get killed during the match in Food Fight Limited Time Mode don't worry, like regular multiplayer modes in other videogames you'll respawn on the map a few seconds later to

re-join the fight. In fact, dying in a match isn't a bad thing at all – if you're smart you can glide all the way into a team's fort and hit them with a surprise attack. But chances are you'll get taken out by an opponent while doing it, so make sure you dole out as much damage as possible with the time you have.

It's Been Coming

Epic Games had been teasing this fantastic food themed mode for some time in the run up to release in late 2018 with a slew of fun things, including Twitter polls and tweaks to the game world map, including two rival food trucks parked next to each other, so this restaurant showdown was clearly something the team had been planning for some time. Like all Limited Time Modes it appeared only for a short stint before disappearing, so here's hoping we see Food Fight again soon! ●

STAY AFLOAT!

Fortnite Battle Royale's Glider Redeploy feature explained!

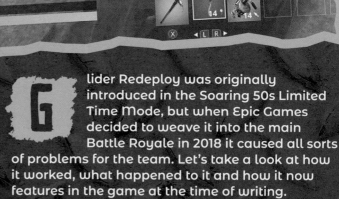

Glider Redeploy was originally introduced in the Soaring 50s Limited Time Mode, but when Epic Games decided to weave it into the main Battle Royale in 2018 it caused all sorts of problems for the team. Let's take a look at how it worked, what happened to it and how it now features in the game at the time of writing.

Basically it allows you to leap off a surface at a height and deploy the glider to stop you crashing to the ground. It was such a success the team opted to include it in all Battle Royale modes.

Bad Plan

However, the new feature didn't exactly go down well with players in the game. Sure, it was a whole lot of fun but many players felt that it upset the balance of the game, in particular during Solo, Duos and Squad Game Modes. You see the original idea behind the Glider Redeploy was to

that the team left it in the game untouched? Either way, Epic Games felt it was best to remove it, so they shelved the ability with the release of Patch 6.3.0. At the time of writing it was still functioning in Playground Mode and other Limited Time Modes.

Despite the fact the ability wasn't working in the main game modes, many believe it will be making a return in some form or another in the future. Until then you can still enjoy using it in any of the supported Limited Time Modes it's included in. ●

allow for better mobility during combat in matches while creating loads of interesting new situations on the battlefield.

That plan backfired because players kept using it to flee from fire-fights. It meant players were losing out on kills and getting frustrated with opponents bailing off a building or a cliff edge at the first sign of trouble. With that, the developers decided to pull it, saying in a blog post "We did not live up to expectations of quickly iterating on the mechanic and communicating plans."

Gone, Not Forgotten

What did you think Fortnite fans? Did you agree with the removal, or would you have preferred

TOYS, TOYS TOYS!

Fortnite fever has well and truly taken hold of the world with the arrival of a slew of collectible action figures, key chains and figurines from some of the world's biggest toy companies, including Funko and McFarlane, the people behind a bunch of highly sought after action figure ranges from the likes of The Walking Dead, Halo and Epic Games' Gears of War. But be warned Fortnite fans - if you want to add them all to your shelves you're going to need really deep pockets...and lots of space!

Some of the most popular collectors items right now are Funko's Pop! Vinyl series. The company has teamed up with Epic Games to release a whole heap of figures based on the game, each one awesomely replicated from the games' 3D modelling. Check 'em all out here and start adding them to your wish lists right now!

5 STAR: FORTNITE

5 star toys for 5 star fans!

TomatoHead

TomatoHead is part of the 5 Star: Fortnite Series 1 collection, and is bound to become something of a collector's item when stocks of this one run dry. TomatoHead first appeared back in April of 2018 as part of Season 4 and quickly became a fan favourite, re-appearing again in Season 5 and 6.

Love Ranger

Who wouldn't want this cute and deadly Love Ranger in their collection? With its huge head, concrete-like skin, stone wings and the super rare Tat Axe Pickaxe, it's both cuddly and terrifying in equal measure. The Love Ranger also comes with an explosive surprise for your friends – the Impulse Grenade! How sweet!

Omega

Of all of the 5 Star: Fortnite range this one is arguably the coolest looking. Omega comes kitted out in full body armour like some sort of comic book super villain. He's clad in a pitch-black skin-suit with terrifying red eyes and the groovy sticky grenade. Add this one to your collection and you'll be the envy of all your friends!

Moonwalker

Released as part of the Space Explorer skin set during Season 3 of Fortnite Battle Royale the Moonwalker 5 Star: Fortnite figure comes clad in a cosy space suit with open helmet showing off the character's face. It also features an EVA Harvesting Tool as well as a small serving of Slurp Juice.

Zoey

Say hello to Zoey, the funky-looking star of Season 4 Sweet Tooth set. Clad in pink top, black leggings with white stripes and her super slick pink nightcap, Zoey is definitely one of the most colourful characters in the 5 Star: Fortnite range. She comes holding the Lollipopper Harvesting Tool and a set of bandages.

POP VINYL!

Big heads for big fans!

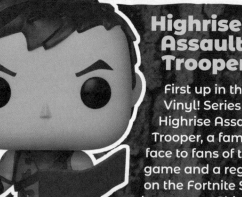

Highrise Assault Trooper

First up in the Pop Vinyl! Series is the Highrise Assault Trooper, a familiar face to fans of the game and a regular on the Fortnite Shop homepage. This guy may not be as rare as the Black Knight, or as awesome as Omega, but we still think he's awesome.

Rex

Roar! Say hello to our little friend, Rex! Part of the Dino Guard set released back in March 2018, this Legendary skin can now be yours in toy form complete with orange bandana and gnarly teeth guaranteed to scare off the other toys as well as the competition. Watch out though, because this one bites!

Dark Voyager

Part of the Space Explorers set that first appeared back in Season 3, the Dark Voyager was a Legendary outfit jazzed up with an orange vest pattern and pitch-black astronaut helmet. Now that it's been made into a Pop! Figure we're pretty sure this one is going to look absolutely amazing on your toy shelf!

Red Nosed Raider

Celebrate Christmas all year round with this awesome holiday themed Pop Vinyl! figure. Replicated exactly as it is in the game, the Red Nosed Raider comes clad in a long-sleeve jumper, red pants and sports a red nose and antlers. Ho-Ho-Ho!

Merry Marauder

Hands up out there anyone who was terrified at the sight of this angry gingerbread man coming running towards you with an assault rifle? Scary right? Well, it seems Pop Vinyl! knew this and transformed the gun-toting terror into a collectible figure! The Marauder would look much cuter if he just learned to smile, right?

PLASTIC FANTASTIC!

Check out the first series of McFarlane Fortnite figures!

Skull Trooper

Everyone loves Skull Trooper, so it's no surprise that McFarlane has decided to immortalize the skin in action figure form. This demented and bone-chilling figure comes packed with a slew of cool items, including Sharp Precision Back Bling, Legendary Bolt-Action Sniper Rifle and the Death Valley Pickaxe. Grab this one before it sells out, folks!

Cuddle Team Leader

Pink fur fans rejoice it's the Cuddle Team Leader! When your friends see this they'll laugh, they'll ogle and probably scream with terror remembering that time you wiped them out using this skin. The figure comes with the Cuddle Bow Back Bling, Legendary Scar Assault Rifle and the Rainbow Smash Pickaxe. Own it!

Black Knight

Whoa! We absolutely love this Black Knight figure from McFarlane! It's no surprise that he was chosen to appear in the first wave of toys; it is one of the rarest character skins in the game. The Black Knight comes complete with Black Shield Back Bling, Grenade Launcher, and the terrifying Axecalibur Harvesting tool.

Rainbow Smash

Essential for all unicorn lovers, this Rainbow Smash replica prop is a whopping 39 inches long, which means it's perfect for fans of Fortnite Cosplay, or those who like to smash their way to victory. With spinning wheels, wild colours and absolutely amazing craftsmanship on behalf of McFarlane this is a must-own!

Raptor

This Raptor figure is sculpted and painted from in-game assets, and comes complete with the mighty Drum Gun, as well as the Icebreaker Pickaxe. Standing at 7 inches tall and billed as the Swiss Army knife of Fortnite Battle Royale character skins, Raptor is guaranteed to look the part on your Fortnite collectible shelf.

PINT-SIZED HEROES

Teeny, tiny two-man squads!

Omega & Valor

Add some pint-sized power to your collection with these two miniscule figures from Funko. Sure, they're small but that doesn't mean that they won't have your back in battle!

Rex & Tricera Ops

These miniaturised versions of Rex and Tricera Ops are so cool we want them in our collection right now! Pop these two next to your Rex Pop Vinyl! figure.

Skull Trooper & Ghoul Trooper

Spook up your collection of Fortnite figures with this double pack that includes Skull Trooper and Ghoul Trooper Pint-sized Heroes. They're teeny, tiny and really, really terrifying!

Black Knight & Red Knight

The Black Knight makes another appearance in our toy round up, this time alongside the Red Knight and in pint-sized form. Grab this double-act before they disappear off shelves forever!

MONOPOLY: FORTNITE EDITION

The world's most famous videogame meets the world's most famous board game!

Holy Moly Fortnite fans! It's the Monopoly: Fortnite Edition, a super addictive board game spin on the most famous videogame in the world.

With gameplay, design and components directly inspired by gameplay mechanics, including map locations and loot chest cards, this is a must-have for any fans of both Fortnite Battle Royale and Fortnite Save The World.

The game comes jam-packed with cool stuff, including 27 character outfit cards that take the form of cardboard outfits with pawn stands, 15 Storm cards, 16 Location cards, 16 loot chest cards, 8 Wall cards, a guide booklet and 110 Health Point Chips, which replace the classic Monopoly money synonymous with the original game.

Once you've chosen your character it's time to throw the die and start the game. This then allows you to pick up health packs, craft walls and dole out damage to other players sitting around the board competing against you.

Monopoly: Fortnite Edition can be played by two to seven players, and is aimed at anyone aged 13 years old and up, so any of our younger readers out there might need to check with their parents before picking up a copy of this one. ●

NERFED

Lock n' load with the Nerf AR-L Blaster!

If playing Fortnite on your console, PC or phone wasn't enough then you'll be super excited to know that you'll be able to play Fortnite for real (kind of) come June 2019 when Nerf's AR-L Blaster replica gun arrives on store shelves.

The stylish plastic rifle features a 10-dart magazine and requires four AA batteries. Now, before you start freaking out the darts are made of foam, so getting hit with one won't leave any marks, but just remember if you do pick this one up and decided to recreate classic battles from the game never aim for someone's face!

At the moment this is currently the only Nerf gun replica created by the toy maker and Epic Games, but don't be surprised if we see more announced in the run up to, and after the initial release of the AR-L Blaster. ●

FORTNITE

FORTNITE
BATTLE
ROYALE